THE INDEX CHART

INDEX
1941=100

150
125
100
75
50
25
0

CHARTER
BUSES

1941   1945   1949

THE LOGARITHMIC CHART

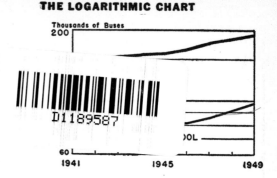

Thousands of Buses
200

60

OOL

1941   1945   1949

THE SUBDIVIDED COLUMN

Thousands of Buses
200
150
100
50
0

REVENUE

SCHOOL

1941   1943   1945   1947   1949

THE PAIRED BAR

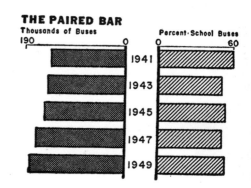

Thousands of Buses   Percent School Buses
190   0   0   60

1941
1943
1945
1947
1949

BAR and SYMBOL

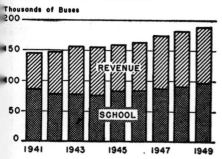

Thousands of Buses
0   25   50   75   100

OOL

AL

RCITY

RTER &
TSEEING

1945
1949

THE COLUMN and CURVE

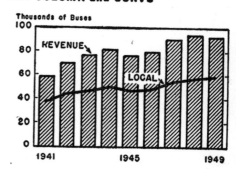

Thousands of Buses
100
80
60
40
20
0

REVENUE

LOCAL

1941   1945   1949

PICTORIAL SURFACE

THOUSANDS OF INTERCITY BUSES
40
30
20
10
0

1941   1945   1949

THE PIE CHART

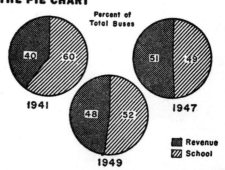

Percent of
Total Buses

40 60
1941

51 49
1947

48 52
1949

Revenue
School

CHARTING STATISTICS

CHARTING
STATISTICS

Mary Eleanor Spear

*Visual Information Specialist, Bureau of Labor
Statistics, United States Department of Labor;
Graphic Consultant and Illustrator; Lecturer,
The American University, Washington, D.C.*

McGRAW-HILL BOOK COMPANY, INC.

New York   Toronto   London

1952

PREFACE

This is a book on practical graphic presentation of statistical data, depicting not only types of charts and their appropriate use, but also subject matter of economic interest.

Each chart in this book was made specifically to exemplify some particular manner of graphically expressing data. Sources have been given throughout for the convenience of the reader who may wish to obtain further information.

Many of the examples in this volume have been selected from problems encountered during years of analyzing and presenting data for the Bureau of Labor Statistics of the United States Department of Labor, for the Treasury Department, The White House, the Office of Defense Mobilization, other Federal agencies, various congressmen, Senate and House committees, labor unions, business groups, associations, and private individuals.

The charts have been kept in simple form to emphasize and define the characteristics which make each one suitable for a certain definite purpose. The lettering on the charts was made with mechanical guides and commercial paste-up type, because these methods are used in the majority of drafting rooms. Different styles of type show the variety available.

The illustrations at the beginning of each chapter and on the end papers give different graphic interpretations and analyses based on the same table. After the basic charts have become familiar, the layouts can be stylized for more dramatic presentation. Imagination is priceless, provided it is used to obtain a new arrangement without distortion of facts, and provided the results are pleasing.

Some points which may seem elementary have been explained in detail because they are the ones that have come up most often in teaching graphic presentation of statistics and in advising authors, statisticians, and economists as to the type of chart to use. It has been attempted to stress the fact that there are particular types of charts to show certain data to advantage, and further, that certain data are better left in tabular form. Frequently the tables from which the graphs were plotted have been included so that the basis of different types of charts would be clearly understood. In some cases numbers in tables have been rounded for convenience.

For those who will use this volume as a basis for teaching graphic presentation of statistics, it is suggested that a simple kit of drafting supplies will facilitate the laying out of charts. The student should have: a drawing board (12 inches by 17 inches); T square (18 inches); triangle 30 by 60° (8 inches); triangle 45° (6 inches); engineer's triangular scale (12 inches); red, blue, green lead pencils (very hard) for plotting; art gum; 1-inch Scotch drafting tape; Nos. H and F drafting pencils. Later, ruling pens, lettering pens (mechanical and hand), shading papers, and other commercial materials and instruments mentioned in the text may be added. Each basic type of chart and its use is illustrated, and further examples can be laid out in class and at home from similar data. Having the students work out each problem will ensure their mastery of the subject.

It is hoped that this book will be of genuine help to all those who are interested in presenting a visual message to specialized audiences and to the general public, as well as to teachers and students in this provocative field.

MARY E. SPEAR

Washington, D.C.
May, 1952

TABLE OF CONTENTS

10 · DUPLICATING, COLOR, TELEVISION   233

Reproduction in Black and White; Color Reproduction; The Chart in Color; Color Blindness; Methods of Applying Color; Color on the Negative; Color on Acetate; Television; Charts and Titles on TV; Reflection of Light; Animation; Use of Color on TV.

LIST OF TABLES

1 • GRAPHIC PRESENTATION

TABLE	School	Local	Intercity	Other	Total
REVENUE MOTOR BUSES *and SCHOOL BUSES*					
1943	77.9	45.6	28.5	2.0	154.0
1944	75.5	48.5	28.0	3.3	155.3
1945	83.2	46.0	29.0	1.0	159.2
1946	82.5	47.8	30.3	1.5	162.0
1947	85.9	54.1	31.9	3.0	174.9
1948	90.4	57.2	31.8	3.2	182.6 EST.

IN THOUSANDS

Source: Automobile Facts and Figures

GRAPHIC PRESENTATION

Graphic presentation is a functional form of art as much as modern painting or architectural design. The painter studies his subject to determine what colors and style and design will best express his ideas. The same kind of imagination is exercised by the graphic artist and analyst.

In addition, the graphic analyst has some of the same problems as the architect. The modern architect studies the family, its hobbies, interests, ambitions, and financial status, among other things, before he designs the new home. The graphic analyst should make just as thorough a study of the characteristics of the data and the uses for which it is intended before he designs his project. In the same way that the architect must know his materials and how they can best be used both in traditional ways and in new ways of his own devising, so must the graphic analyst be familiar with materials and techniques.

The chart has long been recognized as the clearest and most effective method of interpreting and presenting a subject visually. Of equal or even greater importance is the fact that such a chart can also clarify a complex problem. It can reveal hidden facts that were not obvious from the original data.

A graph is also an important means of detecting mistakes in statistical compilations and reckonings. It is a common experience for statistical analysts and researchers in scientific fields to find that when data are charted, errors and omissions that had previously been overlooked are discovered.

In the present day, when visual education in all aspects has become, not only an aid to, but also a vital basis of learning, our attention is called more than ever before to the almost limitless possibilities in this field. The eye absorbs written statistics, but only slowly does the brain receive the message hidden behind the written words and numbers. The correct graph, however, reveals that message briefly and simply. Its purposes, which follow, are clear from its content:

1. Better comprehension of data than is possible with textual matter alone.

2. More penetrating analysis of subject than is possible in written text.

3. A check of accuracy.

This triple purpose of the chart can be carried out through careful planning and familiarity with the functions of all types of graphs and media. The following six steps are fundamental to the development of graphic presentation that will describe statistical data with clarity and dramatic impact.

1. Determine the significant message in the data.

2. Be familiar with all types of charts and make the correct selection.

3. Meet the audience on its own level; know and use all appropriate visual aids.

4. Give detailed and intelligible instructions to the drafting room.

5. Know the equipment and skills of the drafting room.

6. Recognize effective results.

Amplification of these steps is given in the pages which follow.

Selecting the Message

1. *Determine the significant message in the data.* The message is the objective and should not be lost sight of at any stage from the initial planning to the final result. For example:

The president of Department Store, Inc., wishes to emphasize the steady increase of sales since 1940. To stress this point in a direct manner a simple surface chart is used. In the chart, Fig. 1-1, the shaded area accents the trend and gives impact to his message.

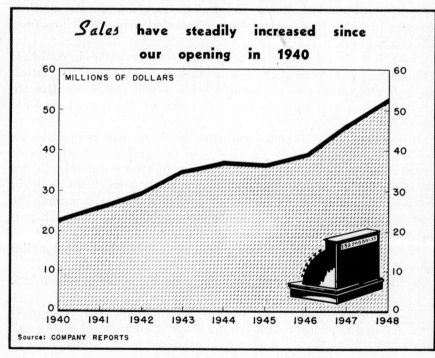

Fig. 1-1. The surface chart adds emphasis.

If, on the other hand, the message is more clearly expressed as a statement, a graph should not be used. Too often presentations are made that
add confusion to the meaning, and a chart is made just for the sake of
making a chart.

The statement "The company cafeteria was used by 9 out of 10 employees during the fiscal year 1949" is sufficient in its meaning and does
not need the 100% pictorial bar to support it (see chart, Fig. 1-2). The
picture with dot overlay adds nothing to the statement, and the necessity
of translating the amount in the title into a percentage on the bar is
likely to confuse the reader.

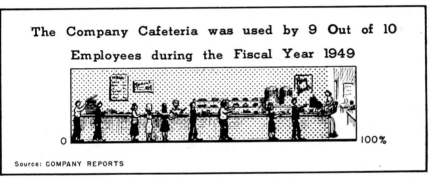

Fig. 1-2. An unnecessary chart.

Types of Charts

2. *Be familiar with all types of charts and make the correct selection.* The message having been decided upon, the next step is to choose the correct type of chart. For this it is necessary to be familiar with the basic types (see inside front and back covers). The more commonly used charts based on *graphic form* are: line, surface, column, bar, pie, and statistical map. Those based on *scale arrangement* are: multiple-time, multiple-amount, and logarithmic. Ability and judgment must be developed to select the type that best presents the message in a clear, concise, and direct manner. For example, a contractor in Baltimore, Maryland, would like to present a broad picture of the valuation of building construction in that city from 1929 through 1950 (see Table 1-1). In this picture he would like to emphasize residential building and show a sharp delineation of the trends.

Figure 1-3 is a *subdivided-column* (component column) chart, which gives the over-all picture and stresses the amount of residential building by showing it as the first component next to the base line. At the same time it emphasizes the fluctuations of the trends.

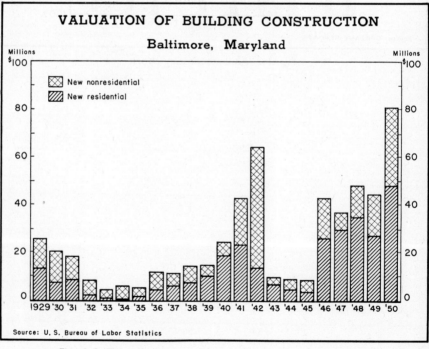

Fig. 1-3. The subdivided column gives a general picture.

TABLE 1-1. PERMIT VALUATION OF BUILDING CONSTRUCTION
BALTIMORE, MARYLAND

	New Non-residential building	New residential building
1929	$11,651,900	$13,302,200
1930	12,826,185	7,240,800
1931	9,429,600	8,363,000
1932	5,883,980	2,069,000
1933	3,116,500	595,000
1934	4,789,127	463,000
1935	2,949,515	1,930,000
1936	6,306,500	4,581,000
1937	4,621,037	6,191,700
1938	6,199,809	7,338,220
1939	3,950,160	10,210,535
1940	5,711,170	18,778,975
1941	19,098,975	23,116,737
1942	49,551,879	13,633,236
1943	2,646,419	6,365,890
1944	4,359,984	3,982,639
1945	4,425,478	3,290,950
1946	16,316,335	25,896,990
1947	6,776,873	29,243,740
1948	12,749,975	34,433,030
1949	17,065,926	26,875,900
1950*	32,701,289	47,672,805

* Preliminary.
Source: U.S. Bureau of Labor Statistics.

If, however, the purpose of his message were the comparison of trends in new nonresidential and new residential building, a *multiple-curve* chart would give a better picture of the breakdown and permit precise measurement of both components (see chart, Fig. 1-4).

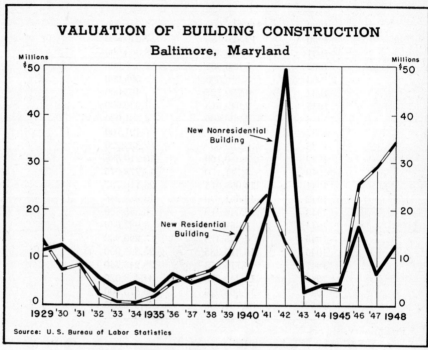

Fig. 1-4. Multiple curves compare trends.

His story could be further developed by plotting total residential and nonresidential construction as a third line.

It is important to keep all presentations straightforward with the particular message pointed up. Do not try to tell too much on one chart.

Analysis of Audience

3. *Meet the audience on its own level; know the use of all visual aids.* Who is your audience? What is the purpose of the meeting? How many will be present? How familiar are they with your subject? Is it a local or out-of-town meeting? What facilities are there for exhibiting your display?

These questions will help you decide whether wall charts, panel exhibits, mechanical displays, film strips, turnover talks, or other visual aids will serve best. For example:

The president calls a meeting of the department heads to plan a sales campaign. There will be ten persons present. What visual aid would be most effective?

Either a table turnover chart book (as in Fig. 1-5) or separate charts about 15 by 20 inches could be seen by this small group and would be easy to handle. Worked out in black and white, or in color symbols that reproduce, the charts could then be economically photostated and a copy given to each supervisor for future use.

This same story told to all the employees in the assembly hall should be displayed on large, legibly lettered charts about 32 by 45 inches. If projection facilities are available, the story could be put on slides or made into a film strip and projected on a screen. Reproduction of the campaign plans for distribution to this larger audience would require offset or multilith process (see Chapter 10).

Fig. 1-5. Using the turnover chart book.

Instructions to Draftsman

4. *Give detailed and intelligible instructions to the drafting room.* Tell the draftsman all of the facts, the message to be conveyed, the audience, the place, how the chart or exhibit is to be used, type of reproduction, and exact deadline. Data should be accompanied by a rough sketch showing the type of chart to help the draftsman grasp the idea quickly.

Tell the draftsman:

Fig. 1-6a. The message to be stressed (the type of chart to be made).

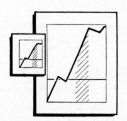

Fig. 1-6b. The audience (the size of the chart).

Fig. 1-6c. How it is to be used (the type of visual aid).

Fig. 1-6d. The place (the material on which to make the chart).

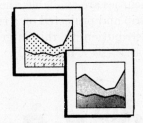

Fig. 1-6e. How it is to be reproduced (black and white, color, or proper shading material to be used).

Fig. 1-6f. The page size, if reproduced (the proportion to make the original chart).

Fig. 1-6g. The exact deadline (the amount of time allowed for making the charts).

Be sure that the facts selected are precisely what you want to stress and the data are correct and final. There will, of course, be many times when final data are not available until the last moment. In this case give the drafting room an estimated figure in order that adequate scale allowance may be made. If chart is to be reproduced, give exact page size, so that the draftsman may make chart in the proper proportion.

If a sketch accompanies data, see that the scales are adequate. Often the draftsman will accept the layout, only to find that one or two figures are above the scale limitation indicated on the sketch.

When the half-tone screen or Ben Day[1] is to be used in reproduction, outline the portion to be shaded and indicate density of shading. Deep tints or "colors" may be used for shadow effect and for filling in columns, bars, or areas, but when the half tone covers plottings and legends, the screen should be kept light so that information on the chart can be read. Compare Charts *A* and *B* in Fig. 1-7.

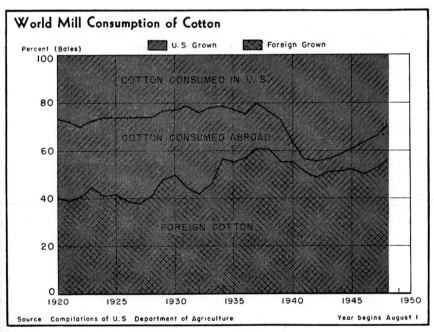

Fig. 1-7A. Wrong use of half-tone screen.

---

[1] See Chapter 10.

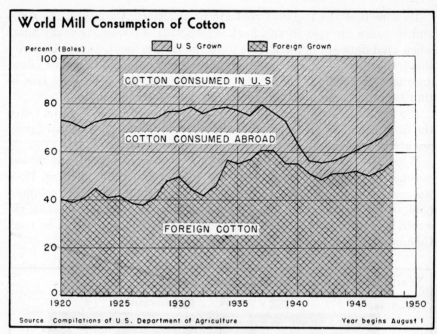

Fig. 1-7B. The right degree of shading.

Equipment

5. *Know the equipment and skills of the drafting room.* It is well to know what commercial materials are stocked in the drafting room. Many printed shading patterns, such as Craftint papers, Zip-a-Tone, and Visitype, can be used effectively for inexpensive reproduction. Sheet or roll acetate gives the opportunity for making overlays on base charts in order to elaborate on a story (see Fig. 1-8).

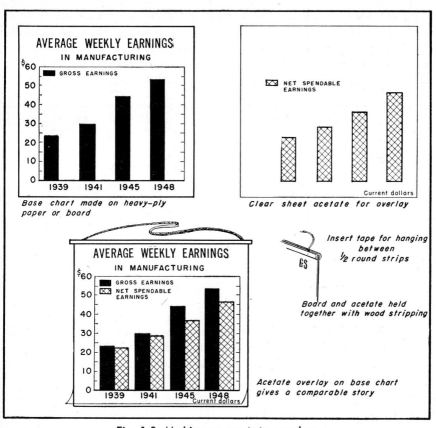

Fig. 1-8. Making an acetate overlay.

Numerous mechanical lettering devices, stack-type, and stick-on letters will give a great variety of sizes and styles of lettering.

Often lack of material or equipment may be the cause of not giving exactly the desired style. This does not mean that the type of chart should be changed, but that the style of layout must be adapted to the lettering device or material that is in the drafting room. Reproduction process will also control choice of these drafting materials.

Figure 1-9*A* shows Leroy lettering and hand crosshatching. This is suitable for photostating and offset processes. Figure 1-9*B* is an example of Fototype lettering and Visitype shading. This is more suitable for multilithing and offset printing, as negatives or plates may be retouched, blocking out excess lines caused by paste-on lettering.

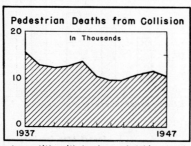

Leroy title with hand crosshatching; good for multilith and photostat reproduction.

A

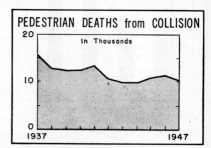

Fototype title with visitype shading; fair for multilith, good for letterpress and lithography reproduction.

B

Fig. 1-9.

Do not ask for airbrushing, silk-screen process, or film retouching if the drafting room is not equipped to handle these techniques. And do not expect special effects, designing, and art work if no qualified artist or designer is on the staff.

Evaluation

6. *Recognize effective results.* Does the type of chart selected give a comprehensive picture of the situation? Does the size of chart and visual aid used satisfy all audience requirements? Do materials meet all reproduction problems? Is the layout well balanced and style of lettering uniform? Does the chart as a whole accurately present the facts? Is the projected idea an effective visual tool?

2 • PLANNING THE CHART

When the type of chart has been selected and the visual aid decided upon, the size of chart layout, lettering, weight of lines, and choice of materials must be carefully considered.

Size of Chart

The exact dimensions of the chart must be given, whether it is to be used in a lecture, for an exhibit, or to appear in print.

If a series of charts are to be used for a table talk, they should be compact and of convenient size to handle. But for a large audience, in order to be legible from a distance, the chart size must be increased to at least the dimensions for an easel talk—about 30 by 40 inches. If possible, it is wise to try out a sample display chart to see if the size is adequate.

If an exhibit is to be planned, the size of the charts may vary, but must conform to the type of visual aid to be used—poster, wall panel, table top, or floor display. If the chart is intended for a limited space, such as a frame in a screen or mechanical device, the exact dimensions of the frame should be given.

If the chart is to be reproduced for publication, the draftsman will lay out his original chart in the proper proportion for reduction to the desired size. This may be done by ratio or by line extension.

Determining the Size by Ratio

Let us assume that the allotted space for the printed chart is 6 inches wide and $3\frac{1}{2}$ inches high. The draftsman wishes to work on an original drawing whose base is 24 inches. The height of the working drawing may be determined by ratio as follows:

$$6 \text{ in. (width)}:3.5 \text{ in. (height)}::24 \text{ in. (width of original)}:X$$
$$\frac{3.5 \times 24}{6} = \frac{84}{6} = 14 \text{ in. (required height)}$$

Or, if the height of the original is 14 inches, the following ratio should be used:

3.5 in. (height):6 in. (width): :14 in. (height of original):X

$$\frac{6 \times 14}{3.5} = \frac{84}{3.5} = 24 \text{ in. (required width)}$$

Thus the original working area drawn 14 inches high and 24 inches at the base will reduce to $3\frac{1}{2}$ by 6 inches, the size of the allotted space.

Line Extension

Lay out a rectangle of the given page size (see part A, Fig. 2-1). Extend the base line to the right to any desired length. Erect perpendiculars at each end of this line. Draw a diagonal through the small rectangle, extending it until it intersects the right-hand perpendicular. This point of intersection will give the enlarged proportional height. A line drawn parallel to the bottom through this intersection will complete the working area of the chart.

Planned Layout

In making the large planned layout in part B, Fig. 2-1, a tentative display dummy was placed in the extreme upper left corner of a piece of bristolboard. The desired depth was laid off, and a base line extended to the right. A line at the top of the layout was drawn parallel to this base. A diagonal from the upper left corner through the original dummy was drawn, and the point of intersection with the base determined the width of the finished work. A perpendicular was then erected at this intersection to the top of the board to complete the enlarged area.

Next, all vertical and horizontal lines of the original dummy were extended by dotted lines to the right edge and base of the dummy, forming points 1, 2, 3, etc. Diagonals were then drawn from the upper left corner through these points to the edge of the enlarged area. By erecting perpendiculars and horizontals at these last points of intersection 1_1, 2_1, 3_1, etc., the height, width, and positions of the different parts of the layout were determined. Thus in Fig. 2-1, part B, points 1-1_1, 2-2_1, 3-3_1, etc. indicate corresponding positions.

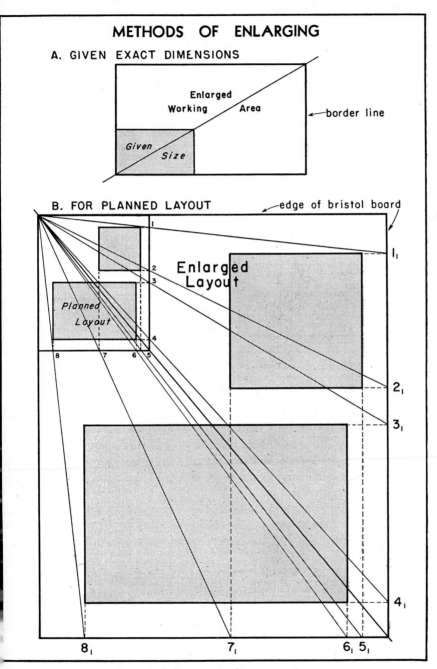

Fig. 2-1. Enlarging by line extension.

Borders

When a border line is used around a chart, all lettering and grid will fall within this area. If no border is used, lettering outside the main grids of the chart should maintain the given page size. (See Fig. 2-2.)

A chart without a border line has several advantages. It is not limited to a designated area. The irregular white space surrounding it makes it more adaptable to any page size. It may be more readily placed either horizontally or vertically on the page, so long as the reduction in the size of the chart does not destroy legibility of lettering.

Fig. 2-2. Size of chart with and without border.

Lettering on Chart

For the standard statistical chart, too many variations in type style are distracting and indicate a lack of planning. In the chart that is not dressed up with art or stylizing, the size of lettering as well as weight of line play an important part in making an effective display. The chart in Fig. 2-3 shows a recommended relationship of lines and lettering in a basic statistical presentation.

The curve label varies in lettering size according to the space left by the trend lines. Shorter wording of the curve label in Fig. 2-3 would warrant a 140 template with a No. 2 pen, rather than the 120-0 used here.

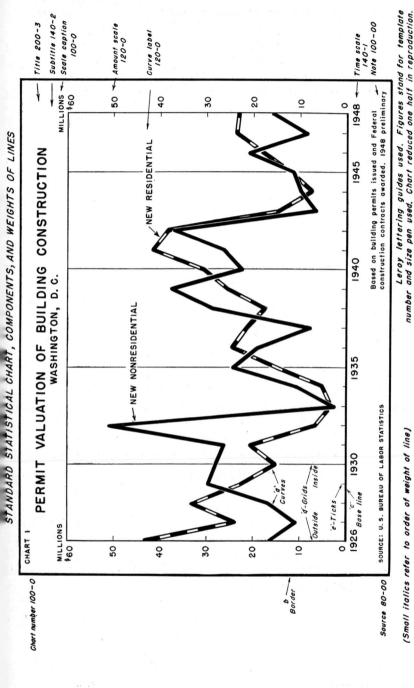

STANDARD STATISTICAL CHART, COMPONENTS, AND WEIGHTS OF LINES

Chart number 100-0

CHART 1

PERMIT VALUATION OF BUILDING CONSTRUCTION
WASHINGTON, D. C.

MILLIONS
$60

50

40

30

20

10

0

1926   1930   1935   1940   1945   1948

SOURCE: U.S. BUREAU OF LABOR STATISTICS

NEW NONRESIDENTIAL

NEW RESIDENTIAL

'a'
Curves

'd'-Grids
Outside   Inside

e-Ticks

'c'
Base line

b
Border

Source 80-00

(Small italics refer to order of weight of line)

Title 200-3

Subtitle 140-2
Scale caption
100-0

MILLIONS
$60

50

40

30

20

10

0

Amount scale
120-0

Curve label
120-0

Time scale
140-1
Note 100-00

Based on building permits issued and Federal
construction contracts awarded. 1948 preliminary

Leroy lettering guides used. Figures stand for template
number and size pen used. Chart reduced one-half in reproduction.

Fig. 2-3. The standard statistical chart, components, and weight of lines. Reduced one-half.

A chart may lose this effectiveness by too-large or too-small lettering, or by overheavy or overlight line drafting. Figure 2-4A shows part of a rough draft as submitted to the drafting room; B is the first inked layout and illustrates how a scale that is too heavily lettered can overbalance the chart proper. Part C has been redrafted and presents a better relationship between lettering and line drafting. In this type of chart the trend label is more effective on the slope of the line.

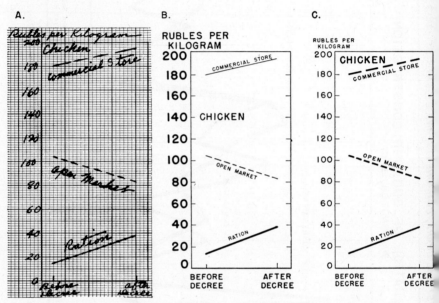

Fig. 2-4. Size of lettering.

In the basic statistical chart, the size of the lettering should be proportional to its importance on the chart. Figure 2-3 shows the recommended sizes ranging from the main title to the source or notes. These are described in the following numbered paragraphs.

1. The *main title* should convey the subject of the graph at a glance

2. The *subtitle* supports the main title and carries essential detail, such as date, index base, or limits of coverage. Do not depend on the text of the article or report to give basic information about your chart. The chart itself should include the facts.

3. The *curve labels* identify the plotted data. At times it may be necessary to carry a legend or key instead of labeling curves or bars directly. This legend should be distinct and easily identified. On a multiple-curve chart when numerous lines intersect, avoid labeling curves where they cross, as it is not immediately clear to which curve the label refers.

On the chart in Fig. 2-5, the "Food" label is better placed in the upper position than where it appears lower down.

4. *Labeling of the grid* on both the horizontal and vertical scales is next in importance. The amount-scale numerals should be directly opposite the horizontal grid. This grid should be divided into units of 1, 2, some multiple of 5, or denary multiples. Avoid dividing a scale into units of 3, 6, 7, 8, or 9.

In labeling the units of the time scale, care should be exercised to place the designation directly under the plotted point, whether the data are plotted on the line or in the space. Each method of plotting is illustrated in Fig. 2-6.

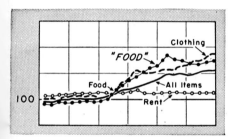

Fig. 2-5. Label curves legibly.

Fig. 2-6. Label time scale beneath plotted point.

5. *Scale captions* indicating the units of value and periods of time should run horizontally on both scales. As a rule, one or two words are sufficient and details can be carried by the subtitle, legend, or note.

The amount-scale caption should state the unit of the scale briefly as pounds, dollars, barrels, etc. When large numbers are plotted, thousands, millions, billions may be added to the scale unit, that is, as "barrels (thousands)" or "thousands of barrels."

Keep the scale simple and use as few zeros as possible. An amount scale going up from 0 to 6 and captioned "millions of dollars" is much easier to read than one progressing to 600 and labeled "tens of thousands of dollars."

6. Finally, the *source and the notes* are in smaller, but legible lettering. The source, indicating the origin of the data, as a rule appears at the bottom left corner. Notes should be reduced in wording to a minimum and appear at the bottom right corner. These may be slightly larger than the source and in upper and lower case to facilitate reading (see chart, Fig. 2-3).

Misspelled Words

Always check the spelling on the finished chart very carefully. The draftsman often overlooks his own misspelling because his concern is with the spacing and forming of the individual letters. You will save yourself many embarrassing moments if you will mentally spell each word as you check the chart.

Weight of Line

The lines on a chart should vary from the heavy curve to the light tick or stub.

The *curve* or curves should be the most striking weight of line on the chart. A curve that is relatively smooth should be heavier than one with active movement. If there are two or more curves on one chart, they should be lighter than if there were a single curve. Even though the curve is heavier than any other drawn element, it should not overpower the rest of the line work (see chart, Fig. 2-7).

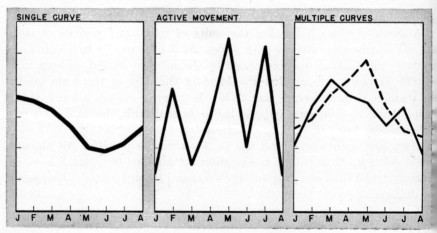

Fig. 2-7. Weight of curve.

When a symbol curve is compared with a solid-line curve, it should be slightly wider and the symbol pattern strongly defined. It will then visually appear in the same importance.

If a *border* is used to frame the chart, it should be next in weight. A single line is best, as it will emerge sharp and even. Double-line borders, if not properly drafted, have a tendency to run together when reproduced, or the lighter of the two lines may appear uneven or broken at intervals.

The line of reference or *base line* is next, whether it is the zero line on an amount chart, or the 100 line of an index chart. However, on a column, bar, or band chart, the base line should be heavy enough to compensate for the larger inked areas.

Grid rulings are next in weight. The outside grid lines are slightly heavier than the inner grid or scale rulings.

The number of rulings is determined by the purpose of the chart, the degree of reading accuracy required, and the type and style of the chart. Usually the only scale lines drawn are those needed to guide the eye for reading the approximate evaluation of the plotted data. Attention must be focused on the curves, and too many grid lines tend to obscure them.

In a single-trend or multiple-curve chart, when a total curve and two or more component curves are plotted against each other, the grid may stop at the total curve. This gives a sharper outline to the total trend (see chart 2A in Fig. 2-8). But in a multiple-trend chart, when two or more categories of equal importance are plotted, the grid should extend to the top of the chart as in 2B. On chart 1B of Fig. 2-8 the rise of petroleum is lost when the grid stops at the "coal" trend, as the eye follows the silhouette of that curve.

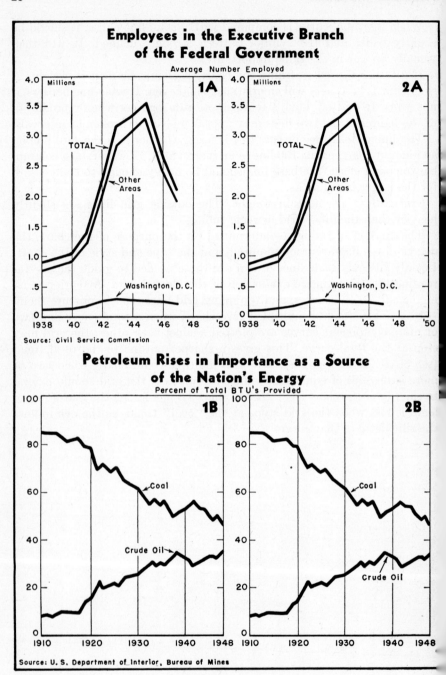

Fig. 2-8. When to complete the grid.

Optical illusions frequently appear in plotting and cause plotted points of the same value to appear higher or lower than the actual value. When this occurs, grid lines permit a more accurate reading.

In Fig. 2-9, the 1940 and 1945 plotted points are identical, but because of the angle of the lines in part *A*, the 1945 readings on the two curves appear to be further separated than the 1940 readings. The grid lines in part *B* help to correct this illusion.

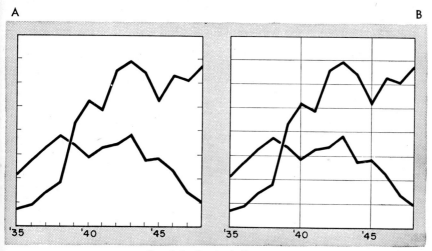

Fig. 2-9. Optical illusions.

Ticks and stubs indicating scale units should be of the lightest weight, and not too long or numerous.

Arrows used to label curves vary with style of chart. They appear best if drawn at right angles to the curve and of fairly light weight. When heavily shaded or overemphasized, they become confusing (see chart, Fig. 2-10).

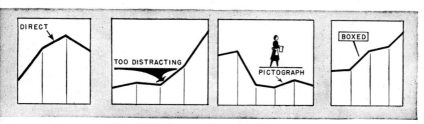

Fig. 2-10. Arrows for identification.

The degree of reduction or enlargement determines the weight of all line work on any chart, diagram, or map. Figure 2-11 shows various weights of line and their corresponding reduced size.

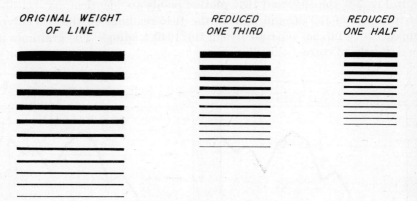

Fig. 2-11. Line reductions.

Line and Surface Symbols

Careful inking of curves, particularly line symbols, and wise choice of shading pattern will facilitate reading and will produce a chart that is attractive to the eye.

In the construction of heavy curves, lines should not extend to a sharp point. A drop-bow pen may be used to control width of line and give a rounded point for more accurate reading. The drop-bow pen is especially designed to draw circles as small as $\frac{1}{32}$ inch in diameter. The width of the curve may be controlled by drawing tangents to these circles. A circle establishes the rounded point on a steep curve. Line symbol patterns must fit the plotted point, or correct trend will be difficult to read (see Fig. 2-12).

Inking In Heavy Curves

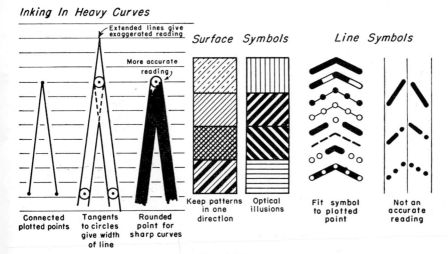

Fig. 2-12.

Crosshatching

When crosshatching is used, the diagonals should slant at a 45-degree angle upward from left to right. All surface patterns should be on the same slant in order to avoid optical illusion. Two diagonals coming together make the column appear to bend; horizontal shading flattens the area; and vertical ruling makes it appear larger. Several shadings used on one chart should be distinctive in pattern, and thus avoid the same tonal quality (see Fig. 2-12).

Some pattern or shading should be applied in each component part of a surface or bar chart. A white space is not only unbalanced in appearance, but often leads to a false interpretation of the data (see Fig. 2-13).

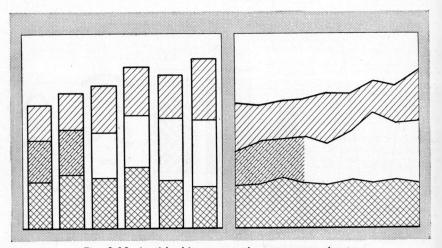

Fig. 2-13. Avoid white spaces in component charts.

Commercial crosshatch materials, such as Visitype and Zip-a-Tone, may be applied to chart surfaces by burnishing on cut-out patterns. Craftint Doubletone or Singletone drawing papers made on Strathmore board may be used. These papers are processed with one or two invisible shading screens. The quick application of Craftint developers either with brush or pen instantly makes shading visible on the chart itself in areas where patterns are desired. About fifty patterns are available.

When commercial patterned materials are not available, fairly accurate crosshatching may be made by using a strip of cross-section paper, a triangle, and a T square. Figure 2-14 illustrates this method.

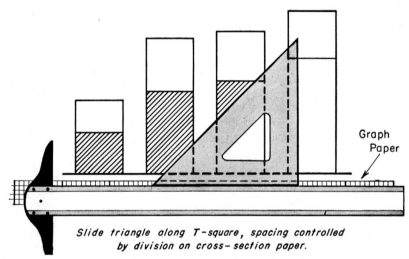

Slide triangle along T-square, spacing controlled by division on cross-section paper.

Fig. 2-14. Method of hand crosshatching.

Scales

Scale selection and shape of grid are most important in chart preparation. As the scale is the controlling factor of presentation, its choice, whether deliberate or accidental, may present an accurate picture or an extremely misleading story. A trend may be exaggerated or minimized, or a given difference may appear greater or less in amount, if either the horizontal or vertical grids are expanded or contracted. See Fig. 2-15, for seven ways of presenting the same data.

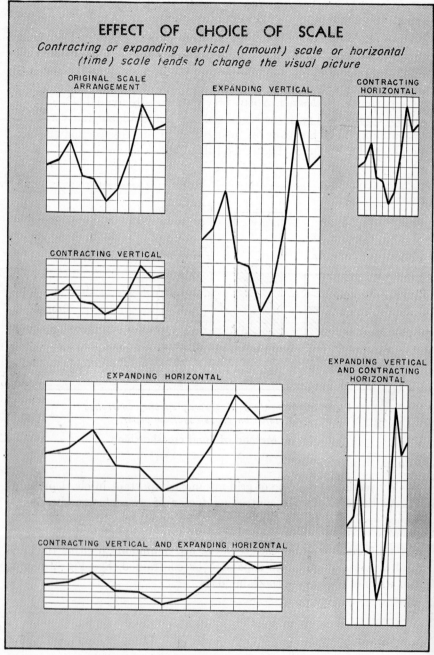

Fig. 2-15. Expanding and contracting the scale.

If it is intended to try to keep a chart up to date, extra space should be allowed on both horizontal and vertical grids. If this is done, the chart will not require remaking for every extension of time and growth of trend.

Breaking the Scale

In line charts with an arithmetic scale, it is essential to set the base line at zero in order that the correct perspective of the general movement may not be lost. Breaking or leaving off part of the scale leads to misinterpretation, because the trend then shows a disproportionate degree of variation in movement.

In Fig. 2-16, charts *A* show how dropping the zero line gives an impression of greater variance. Charts *B*, plotted from 0, give the relevant range of the trend.

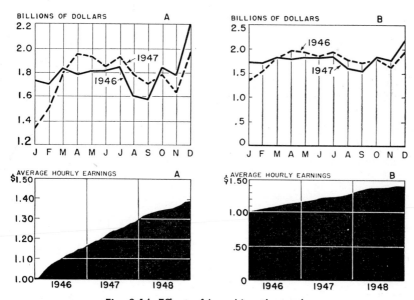

Fig. 2-16. Effect of breaking the scale.

A broken scale should not be used on bar, column, or surface charts, because the true relationship is entirely lost in the resulting distortion. Figure 2-17 shows both the correct and the incorrect way of presenting data.

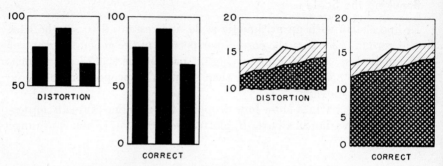

Fig. 2-17. Distortion in column and surface charts.

Grouping Charts

In grouping related charts, comparable scales should be used; otherwise comparisons will be misleading. In Fig. 2-18, charts *1A* and *2A* should have the same scale because they are being compared. In a layout using chart *2A* alone, the scale need only go to 30 billions. If comparison is not significant, each chart may be given an independent scale. Charts *1B* and *2B* in Fig. 2-18 are two different series concerning U.S. National Banks and need not be on the same unit scale.

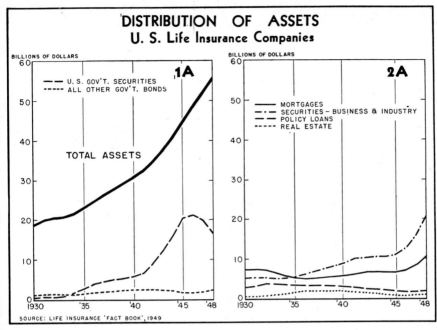

DISTRIBUTION OF ASSETS
U. S. Life Insurance Companies

1A

BILLIONS OF DOLLARS

— — U. S. GOV'T. SECURITIES
- - - ALL OTHER GOV'T. BONDS

TOTAL ASSETS

2A

BILLIONS OF DOLLARS

—— MORTGAGES
—·—· SECURITIES – BUSINESS & INDUSTRY
— — POLICY LOANS
- - - - REAL ESTATE

SOURCE: LIFE INSURANCE 'FACT BOOK', 1949

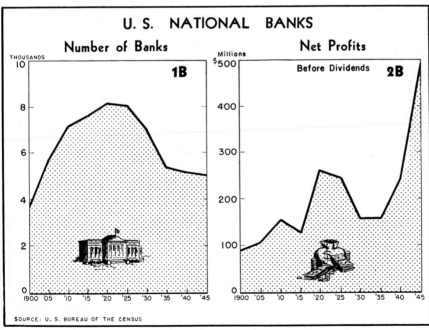

U. S. NATIONAL BANKS

Number of Banks

1B

THOUSANDS

Net Profits

2B

Millions

Before Dividends

SOURCE: U. S. BUREAU OF THE CENSUS

Fig. 2-18. Grouping related charts.

Stylizing should NOT be extreme.

In chart A the graphic idea is clear

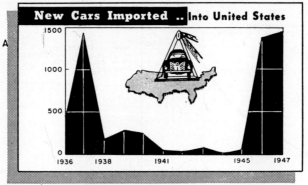

A

B

The over-stylizing in charts
B and C catch the eye,
     But — — —
          The story is lost
in the confusion of design
and shading.

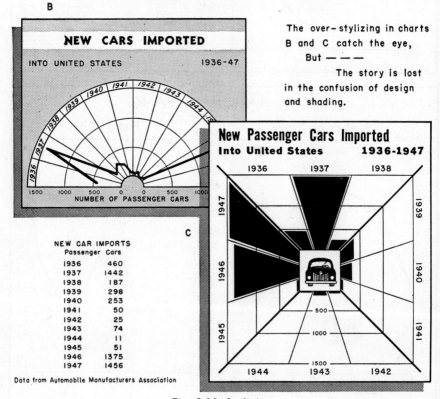

NEW CAR IMPORTS	
Passenger Cars	
1936	460
1937	1442
1938	187
1939	298
1940	253
1941	50
1942	25
1943	74
1944	11
1945	51
1946	1375
1947	1456

Data from Automobile Manufacturers Association

C

Fig. 2-19. Stylizing.

Stylizing

Stylizing a chart should not be attempted unless approved principles of graphic presentation are thoroughly understood. To stylize, you should plan carefully to have:

1. Attractive art work and design.
2. Balanced degree of shading.
3. Uniform style of lettering.

In Fig. 2-19, chart *A*, the data are easily grasped. On the other hand, the message should not be lost or distorted by overdecoration or by freak layouts, as in charts *B* and *C* of the same figure. The purpose of a chart is to display facts—not to disguise them.

3 • LINE CHARTS

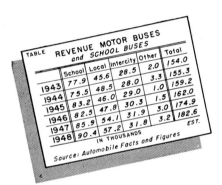

TABLE	REVENUE MOTOR BUSES and SCHOOL BUSES				
	School	Local	Intercity	Other	Total
1943	77.9	45.6	28.5	2.0	154.0
1944	75.5	48.5	28.0	3.3	155.3
1945	83.2	46.0	29.0	1.0	159.2
1946	82.5	47.8	30.3	1.5	162.0
1947	85.9	54.1	31.9	3.0	174.9
1948	90.4	57.2	31.8	3.2	182.6

IN THOUSANDS   EST.

Source: Automobile Facts and Figures

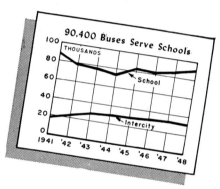

LINE CHARTS

The Curve Chart

The curve or line chart is the most widely used method of presenting statistics graphically. This type of chart is simple to construct. The plotted points of the data are connected by a solid or symbol line. The fluctuation of this line shows the variations in the trend; the distance of the plotting from the base line of the graph indicates the quantity (see chart, Fig. 3-1).

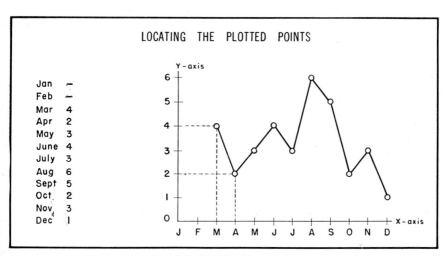

Fig. 3-1. Plotting the curve.

When to Use

The charts in Fig. 3-2 illustrate six of the principal uses of the curve chart:

1. *When the emphasis is on the movement rather than on the actual amount (A).*

2. *When several series are compared on the same chart (B).*

3. *When data cover a long period of time (C).*

4. *When a frequency distribution is presented by two or more curves (D).*

5. *When a multiple-amount scale is used (E).*

6. *When estimates, forecasts, interpolation, or extrapolation are to be shown (F).*

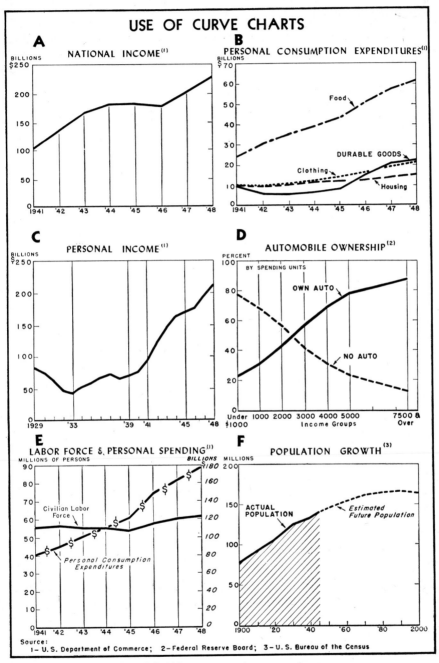

Fig. 3-2. When to use the curve chart.

Plotting the Point

The question often arises as to whether the data should be plotted on the line or in the space between the vertical rulings.

As a rule, point data, or data for the first or last of the month, or monthly and yearly totals are plotted on the line.

Period data, that is, data for the average of a segment of time or the mid-point of a designated time span, are plotted in the space between the vertical rulings.

However, in the following exceptions, period data are plotted on the line:

1. *When data cover a long span of time.* In this case plottings would be so close together that it would be of no importance whether the plotted point were on the line or in the space. The data in the chart, Fig. 3-3, is as of August 31 of each year. Because of the length of time covered, it is plotted on the line.

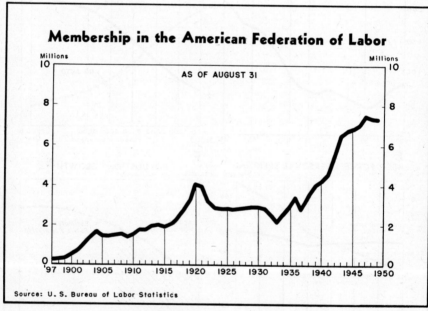

Fig. 3-3. Plotting a long period of time.

TABLE 3-1. Membership in the American Federation of Labor

Period	Total membership (thousands)	Period	Total membership (thousands)
1897	265	1924	2,866
1898	278	1925	2,877
1899	349	1926	2,804
1900	548	1927	2,813
1901	788	1928	2,896
1902	1,024	1929	2,934
1903	1,466	1930	2,961
1904	1,676	1931	2,890
1905	1,494	1932	2,532
1906	1,454	1933	2,127
1907	1,539	1934	2,608
1908	1,587	1935	3,045
1909	1,483	1936	3,422
1910	1,562	1937	2,861
1911	1,762	1938	3,623
1912	1,770	1939	4,006
1913	1,996	1940	4,247
1914	2,021	1941	4,569
1915	1,946	1942	5,483
1916	2,073	1943	6,564
1917	2,371	1944	6,807
1918	2,726	1945	6,931
1919	3,260	1946	7,152
1920	4,079	1947	7,578
1921	3,907	1948	7,221
1922	3,196	1949	7,241
1923	2,926		

Source: U.S. Bureau of Labor Statistics and Brookings Institution.

2. *When two or more curves are plotted at varying intervals.* In the chart, Fig. 3-4, some of the data were plotted monthly and some quarterly.

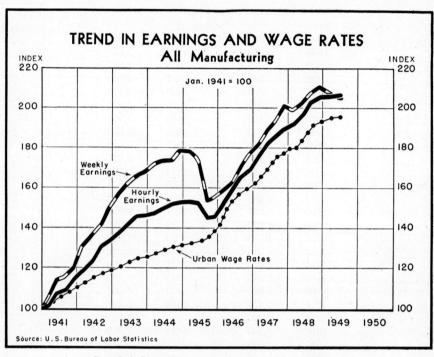

TREND IN EARNINGS AND WAGE RATES
All Manufacturing

Jan. 1941 = 100

Weekly Earnings

Hourly Earnings

Urban Wage Rates

1941 1942 1943 1944 1945 1946 1947 1948 1949 1950

Source: U.S. Bureau of Labor Statistics

Fig. 3-4. Plotting trends at irregular intervals.

3. *When data are cumulative.* Note cumulated Table 3-2 used for plotting the chart, Fig. 3-5.

4. *When a step or staircase chart is plotted,* showing frequency distribution, as in the chart, Fig. 3-6.

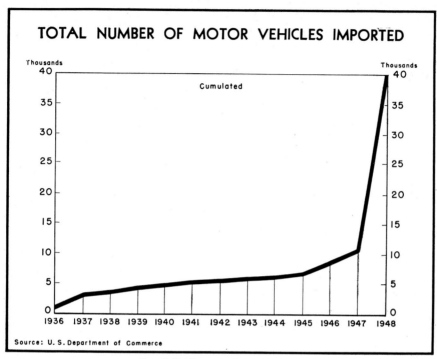

Fig. 3-5. The cumulated curve.

TABLE 3-2. TOTAL NUMBER OF MOTOR VEHICLES IMPORTED, 1936–1948

Year	Total for year	Cumulated
1936	1,068	1,068
1937	1,941	3,009
1938	578	3,587
1939	634	4,221
1940	555	4,776
1941	358	5,134
1942	424	5,558
1943	350	5,908
1944	326	6,234
1945	531	6,765
1946	1,965	8,730
1947	2,124	10,854
1948	29,112	39,966

Source: U.S. Department of Commerce.

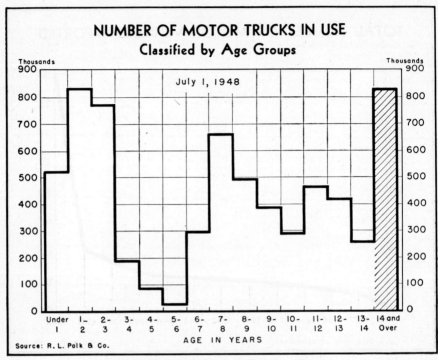

Fig. 3-6. The step or staircase chart.

TABLE 3-3. Number of Motor Trucks in Use
Classified by age group as of July 1, 1948

Age, years*	Number (thousands)	Age, years*	Number (thousands)
Under 1	525	8–9	491
1–2	833	9–10	386
2–3	770	10–11	286
3–4	186	11–12	462
4–5	85	12–13	418
5–6	26	13–14	257
6–7	297	14 and older	828
7–8	662		

* Each class interval includes the lower, but not the higher, age given.
Source: Auto Facts, 1949. R. L. Polk & Co.

Scale Captions

In a time-series chart, the amount- or vertical-scale caption may have many variations. Go carefully over the material before deciding whether

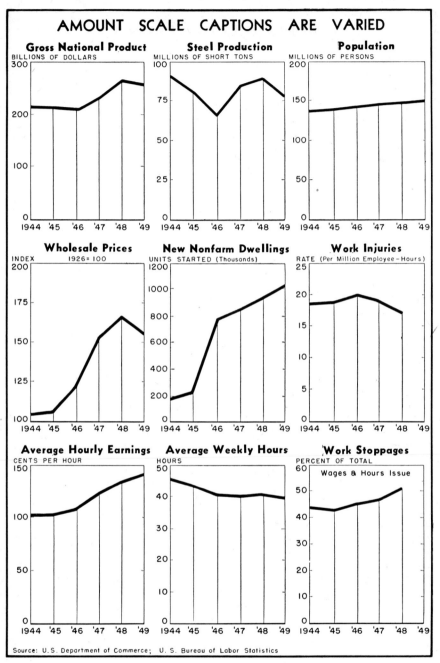

Fig. 3-7. Amount-scale captions.

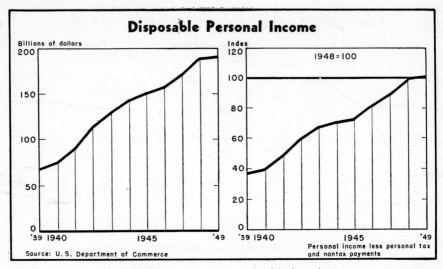

Fig. 3-8. Comparing amount and index charts.

TABLE 3-4. Disposable Personal Income (Billions of Dollars)

		Index 1948 = 100
1939	$ 70.2	36.7
1940	75.7	39.6
1941	92.0	48.2
1942	116.7	61.1
1943	132.4	69.2
1944	147.0	77.0
1945	151.1	79.1
1946	158.1	82.8
1947	172.0	90.1
1948	190.8	100.0
1949*	192.9	101.1

* Estimate based on incomplete data; fourth quarter by Council of Economic Advisors.

Source: U.S. Department of Commerce.

TABLE 3-5. Consumers' Price Index

	1935–1939 = 100	1948 = 100
1939	99.4	58.1
1940	100.2	58.5
1941	105.2	61.4
1942	116.5	68.7†
1943	123.6	73.8†
1944	125.5	75.8†
1945	128.4	77.9†
1946	139.3	83.4†
1947	159.2	93.1†
1948	171.2	100.0
1949*	169.1	98.8

* Estimated through November 15, 1949.

† Adjusted to take account of the understatement.

Source: U.S. Bureau of Labor Statistics.

actual amounts, index, per cent, rate, etc., will best present your story. The charts in Fig. 3-7 show several amount-scale headings.

The Index Chart

The index chart shows the relation of trend to a selected base year or years. To obtain the index numbers for plotting this trend, divide each given amount by the value of the selected base year and multiply the quotient by 100. In the charts, Fig. 3-8, 1948 was chosen as the base year.

Changing Index Base

In the same way a relative or index series may be changed from one base to another by dividing the old index series by the value of the new base. In the charts, Fig. 3-9, when 1948 is used as 100, the trend is shown far below the base line in comparison to the 1935–1939 base.

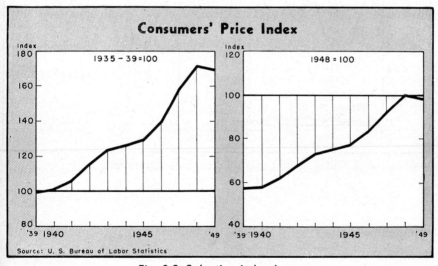

Fig. 3-9. Selecting index base.

When to Use Indexes

Index charts are used to advantage:

1. *For comparing the relationship of two series which differ greatly in amount or quantity.*

In the charts, Fig. 3-10, the difference in the magnitude of the amounts of wheat and rye made the production of rye seem insignificant. However, by translating the actual amounts into indexes, we find that the variation in the production of rye was relatively as great as that of wheat until 1943.

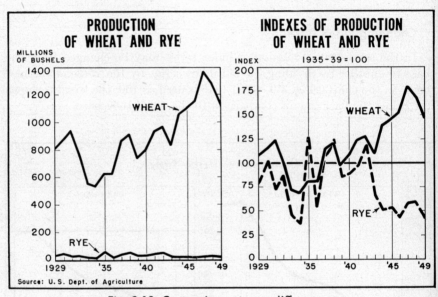

Fig. 3-10. Comparing extreme differences.

TABLE 3-6

Year	Production of wheat and rye (thousand bu.)		Indexes of production of wheat and rye 1935–39 = 100	
	Wheat	Rye	Wheat	Rye
1929	824,183	35,411	108.6	78.8
1930	886,522	45,383	116.8	101.1
1931	941,540	32,777	124.1	73.0
1932	756,307	39,099	99.6	87.0
1933	552,215	20,573	72.7	45.8
1934	526,052	16,285	69.3	36.3
1935	628,227	56,938	82.8	126.7
1936	629,880	24,239	83.0	53.9
1937	873,914	48,862	115.1	108.9
1938	919,913	55,984	121.2	124.6
1939	741,210	38,562	97.6	85.9
1940	814,646	39,725	107.3	88.4
1941	941,970	43,878	124.1	97.7
1942	969,381	52,929	127.7	117.8
1943	843,813	28,680	111.2	63.9
1944	1,060,111	22,525	139.7	50.1
1945	1,108,224	23,952	146.0	53.3
1946	1,153,046	18,879	151.9	42.1
1947*	1,367,000	25,977	180.1	57.8
1948*	1,288,000	26,400	169.6	58.8
1949*	1,129,000	18,800	148.7	41.8

Source: U.S. Department of Agriculture.
* Preliminary.

2. *When the relationship of two or more series of unlike basic units is to be shown.* In the charts, Fig. 3-11, the first graph shows the trend of production of wheat and beef by using a multiple-amount scale; however, in the second graph the relative change in the trends is shown more clearly by converting the amounts to indexes.

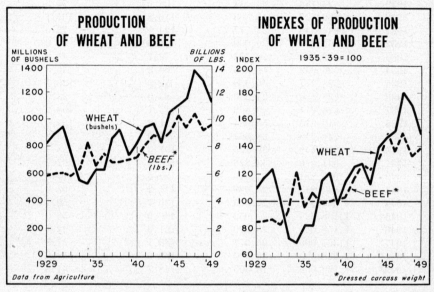

Fig. 3-11. Comparing unlike basic units.

TABLE 3-7

	Production of wheat and beef		Indexes of production of wheat and beef 1935–39 = 100	
Year	Wheat (thousand bu.)	Beef (million lb.)	Wheat	Beef
1929	824,183	5,871	108.6	84.6
1930	886,522	5,917	116.8	85.2
1931	941,540	6,009	124.1	86.6
1932	756,307	5,789	99.6	83.4
1933	552,215	6,440	72.7	92.8
1934	526,052	8,345	69.3	120.4
1935	628,227	6,608	82.8	95.2
1936	629,880	7,358	83.0	106.1
1937	873,914	6,798	115.1	97.9
1938	919,913	6,908	121.2	99.5
1939	741,210	7,011	97.6	101.0
1940	814,646	7,175	107.3	103.4
1941	941,970	8,082	124.1	116.5
1942	969,381	8,843	127.7	127.4
1943	843,813	8,571	111.2	123.5
1944	1,060,111	9,112	139.7	131.3
1945	1,108,224	10,275	146.0	148.1
1946	1,153,046	9,373	151.9	135.1
1947*	1,367,000	10,428	180.1	150.3
1948*	1,288,000	9,181	169.6	132.3
1949*	1,129,000	9,600	148.7	138.3

Source: U.S. Department of Agriculture.
* Preliminary.

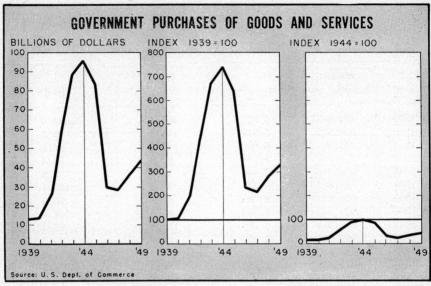

Fig. 3-12. Selection of the base year.

TABLE 3-8. GOVERNMENT PURCHASES OF GOODS AND SERVICES

Year	Billions	Indexes 1939 = 100	1944 = 100
1939	$13.1	100.0	13.6
1940	13.9	106.1	14.4
1941	24.7	188.5	25.6
1942	59.7	455.7	61.9
1943	88.6	676.3	91.8
1944	96.5	736.6	100.0
1945	82.8	632.0	85.8
1946	30.7	234.3	31.8
1947	28.8	219.8	29.8
1948	36.7	280.1	38.0
1949*	43.5	332.0	45.1

* Estimate based on incomplete data; fourth quarter by CEA.
Source: U.S. Department of Commerce.

Selection of Base Year

The selection of the base year is of the utmost importance in stressing or minimizing a particular fact. If the lowest value in the series is selected for the base year, the series will be above the 100 per cent base line, whereas the highest value will bring the series below the 100 line.

In the charts, Fig. 3-12, the 1939-base index makes the 1944 expenditures seem very high. When 1944 is used as the base, the expenditures seem moderate.

As a rule, in historical series, a base year is selected during a time which is considered "normal." Different phenomena and economic events influence this "normal base" selection. A totally different visual story may be presented from the same data because of a difference of opinion or point of view as to what year or period is considered a "normal" base.

For example, a large industry desired to show that existing wages were fair and sufficient when compared to the cost of living. They selected 1939 as a valid year on which to base this conclusion. On the other hand, the workers said that prices had risen so high that January, 1945, should be the base year. Based on Table 3-9, the two charts in Fig. 3-13 depict both points of view.

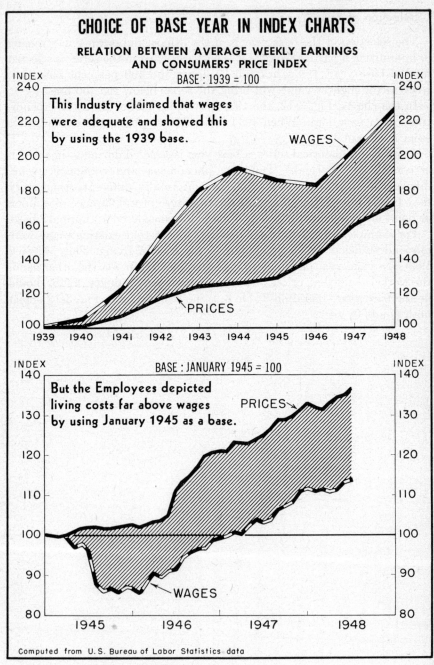

CHOICE OF BASE YEAR IN INDEX CHARTS
RELATION BETWEEN AVERAGE WEEKLY EARNINGS AND CONSUMERS' PRICE INDEX
BASE : 1939 = 100

This Industry claimed that wages were adequate and showed this by using the 1939 base.

WAGES

PRICES

BASE : JANUARY 1945 = 100

But the Employees depicted living costs far above wages by using January 1945 as a base.

PRICES

WAGES

Computed from U.S. Bureau of Labor Statistics data

Fig. 3-13. Effect of changing the base year.

TABLE 3-9. Relation between Average Weekly Earnings and Consumers'
Price Index

1939 = 100

	Average weekly earnings in manufacturing		Consumers' price index
	Dollars	Index	
1939	$23.86	100.0	100.0
1940	25.20	105.6	100.8
1941	29.58	123.9	105.8
1942	36.65	153.6	117.2
1943	43.14	180.8	124.3
1944	46.08	193.1	126.2
1945	44.39	186.0	129.1
1946	43.74	183.3	140.1
1947	49.25	206.4	160.1
1948	54.14	226.9	172.2

January, 1945 = 100

	Index of average weekly earnings				Consumers' price index			
	1945	1946	1947	1948	1945	1946	1947	1948
Jan.	100.0	86.6	99.2	111.3	100.0	102.2	120.6	132.8
Feb.	99.7	85.4	99.6	110.7	99.8	101.9	120.5	131.7
Mar.	99.8	88.7	100.4	111.4	99.7	102.4	122.9	131.3
Apr.	99.2	90.3	100.0	110.7	100.0	103.1	122.8	133.2
May	96.9	89.5	102.0	111.2	100.7	103.6	122.7	134.1
June	97.5	91.1	103.9	113.2	101.5	104.8	123.6	135.0
July	95.8	91.3	103.1	113.6	101.8	111.0	124.6	136.6
Aug.	87.8	94.7	103.5		101.7	113.3	126.1	
Sept.	86.0	95.6	106.3		101.4	114.8	128.8	
Oct.	86.3	96.2	107.4		101.4	116.9	128.8	
Nov.	85.8	96.4	108.0		101.7	119.7	129.7	
Dec.	86.8	98.8	110.9		102.2	120.6	131.3	

Source: U.S. Bureau of Labor Statistics.

The Base Line

Opinions differ as to the importance of starting an index chart at zero. In general, a broader picture can be presented by using the zero line. However, if a multiple-base graph such as is found in stock-market charts is used (chart A, Fig. 3-14), or if variations from the 100-base line constitute the focus of interest (chart B, Fig. 3-14), the grid may be drawn only as large as necessary to accommodate the maximum and minimum variation of trend. Occasionally the amount of space allotted to the chart may be the deciding factor in determining whether or not to use the zero line. In both A and B of Fig. 3-14 the 100 line is accented. In part B the grid lines tend to emphasize the unit labor cost.

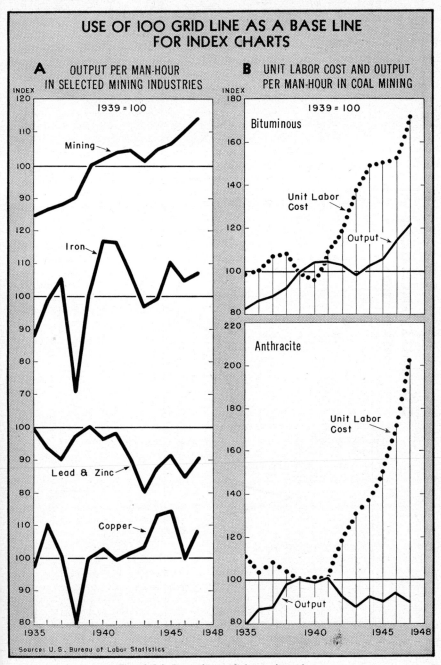

Fig. 3-14. Base line of the index chart.

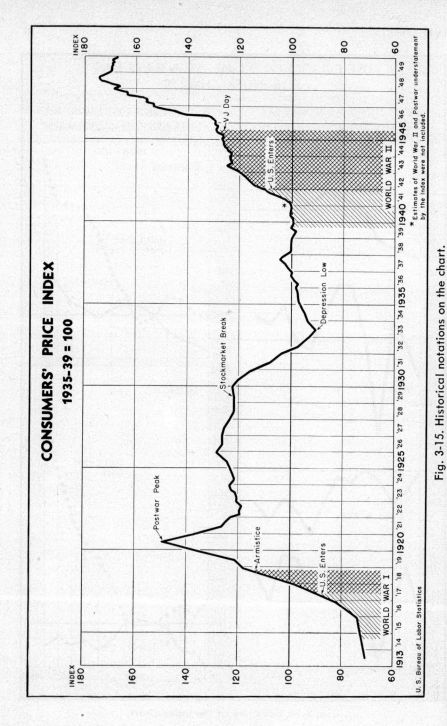

CONSUMERS' PRICE INDEX

1935-39 = 100

Fig. 3-15. Historical notations on the chart.

U. S. Bureau of Labor Statistics

* Estimates of World War II and Postwar understatement
by the Index were not included.

62

Historical Trends

Further interest may be added to the trend chart by noting historical or economic events at selected dates along the curve. This technique is an excellent way of tying the chart very close to the text. For instance, in the chart, Fig. 3-15 the note is further elaborated by the accompanying text carrying the rather involved explanation of the economic event that occurred in 1941. To quote, "The President's Committee on the Cost of Living estimated that, because of quality deterioration, disappearance of cheaper goods, and other factors, the consumers' price index understated the rise in retail prices of living essentials by 3 to 4 points between January, 1941, and September, 1944, for large cities and an additional ½ point for small cities. Later the Stabilization Director, in December, 1945, made an allowance of 4½ points for large cities and 5 points for large and small cities combined.

"These adjustments have not been included by the Bureau in the published indexes. For a more detailed statement concerning these adjustments, see the *Monthly Labor Review* for March, 1947."[1]

It is preferable that a chart be drawn and captioned well enough to stand alone without voluminous explanation, but this is not always possible. In any event, keep the notes and legends to a minimum.

Illustrations

Illustrations will liven up a graph and may add a humorous touch. The little man in the chart, Fig. 3-16, climbing upward, slipping, sitting on top of the peak, and then falling, is expressive of the nature of the trend.

Multiple Curves

Multiple-curve charts compare two or more related trends. If too many curves appear on one chart, the plottings become indistinguishable (see Chart A, Fig. 3-17). Here two or more separate graphs should be made (see B of same figure). When several related charts are made, and it is expected to compare them, the unit scale measurements must be kept the same throughout. This holds true whether actual amounts or index numbers are plotted.

[1] Published by the United States Department of Labor, Bureau of Labor Statistics.

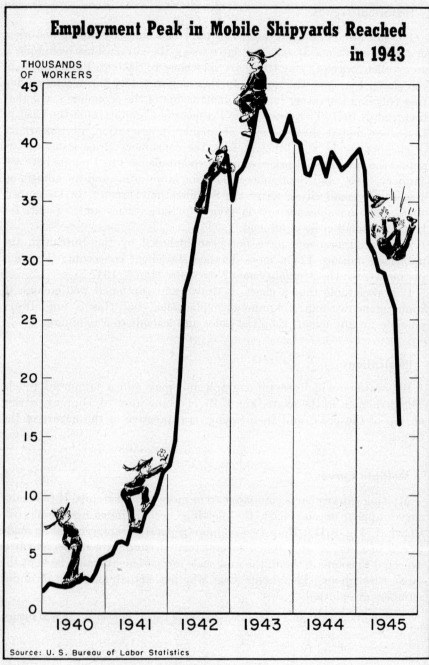

Employment Peak in Mobile Shipyards Reached in 1943

THOUSANDS
OF WORKERS

Source: U. S. Bureau of Labor Statistics

Fig. 3-16. Illustrating the chart.

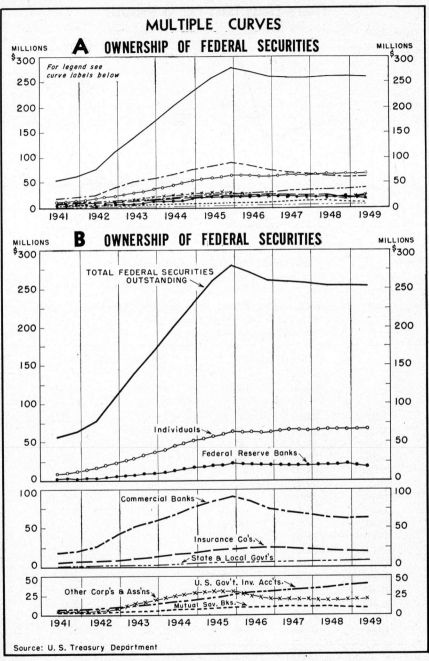

Fig. 3-17. Comparing several trends.

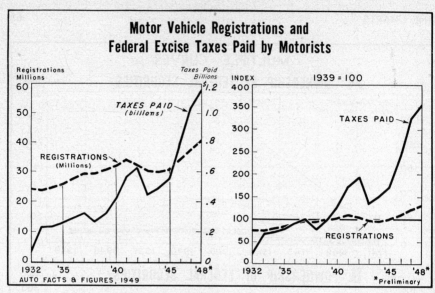

Fig. 3-18. Multiple-amount scales.

TABLE 3-10. MOTOR-VEHICLE REGISTRATIONS AND FEDERAL EXCISE TAXES PAID
BY MOTORISTS
Actual amounts and index (1939 = 100)

	Registrations		Federal excise taxes	
	Millions	Index	Millions	Index
1932	24.1	78.8	$ 75.4	23.2
1933	23.9	78.1	230.6	71.2
1934	25.0	81.7	235.7	72.7
1935	26.2	85.6	256.7	79.2
1936	28.2	92.2	297.1	91.7
1937	29.7	97.0	326.5	100.8
1938	29.4	96.1	268.0	82.7
1939	30.6	100.0	324.0	100.0
1940	32.0	104.6	416.4	128.5
1941	34.5	112.7	572.8	176.8
1942	32.6	106.5	626.1	193.2
1943	30.5	99.7	445.8	137.6
1944	30.1	98.3	486.1	150.0
1945	30.6	100.0	557.0	171.9
1946	33.9	110.8	798.4	246.4
1947	37.4	122.2	1,039.4	320.8
1948	40.6	132.7	1,157.0	357.1

Source: Auto Facts, 1949, U.S. Public Roads Administration, and Internal Revenue
Index computed from given data.

Multiple-amount Scales

Charts with multiple-amount scales, that is, making use of two amount scales for comparing series of unlike units, are not appropriate for popular presentation. The resulting chart is apt to be misinterpreted if the reader is not familiar with this type of graph. Rather than put two or more scales on one chart, it is better to convert the figures to indexes to show relative trends; or the data could be laid out on a logarithmic or ratio scale which would show the rates of change (see charts in Fig. 3-37).

If, however, the problem calls for the use of multiple-amount scales, particular care should be taken to identify the curve with its corresponding unit-amount scale. Both curve label and scale caption should carry the same unit amount or identifying wording (see chart, Fig. 3-19).

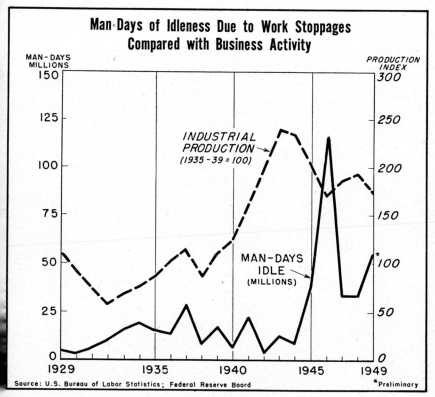

Fig. 3-19. Identify curve with corresponding scale.

This care in matching the curve to its scale should be carried through not only when the chart is made in black and white, but also when it is in color. The charts, Fig. 3-20, show three methods of identifying multiple-amount scales.

In selecting the two-amount scales, the units of each scale should be directly opposite each other. That is, if the left-hand scale is to include the plotted amount of 59 millions, and the right-hand scale is to include 2.4 millions, the left scale should go up by 10's to 60, whereas each right scale unit goes up by .5 to 3.0 (Fig. 3-20).

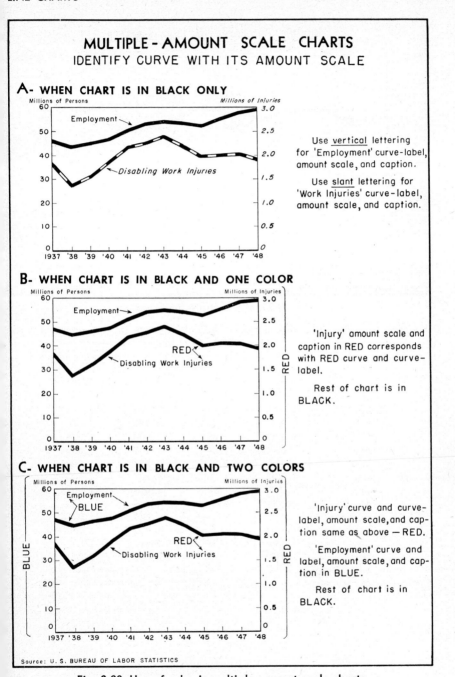

MULTIPLE - AMOUNT SCALE CHARTS
IDENTIFY CURVE WITH ITS AMOUNT SCALE

A- WHEN CHART IS IN BLACK ONLY

Millions of Persons   *Millions of Injuries*

Employment

Disabling Work Injuries

Use <u>vertical</u> lettering for 'Employment' curve-label, amount scale, and caption.

Use <u>slant</u> lettering for 'Work Injuries' curve-label, amount scale, and caption.

B- WHEN CHART IS IN BLACK AND ONE COLOR

Millions of Persons   Millions of Injuries

Employment

RED

Disabling Work Injuries

RED

'Injury' amount scale and caption in RED corresponds with RED curve and curve-label.

Rest of chart is in BLACK.

C- WHEN CHART IS IN BLACK AND TWO COLORS

Millions of Persons   Millions of Injuries

Employment

BLUE

RED

Disabling Work Injuries

BLUE   RED

'Injury' curve and curve-label, amount scale, and caption same as above — RED.

'Employment' curve and label, amount scale, and caption in BLUE.

Rest of chart is in BLACK.

Source: U. S. BUREAU OF LABOR STATISTICS

Fig. 3-20. Use of color in multiple-amount-scale charts.

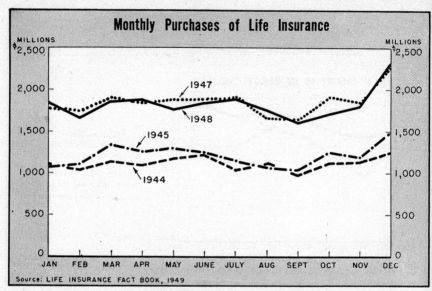

Fig. 3-21. The multiple-time chart.

TABLE 3-11. MONTHLY PURCHASES OF LIFE INSURANCE IN THE UNITED STATES
(MILLIONS OF DOLLARS)
Exclusive of revivals, increases, dividend additions, and reinsurance acquired

	1944	1945	1947	1948
Jan.	$1,115	$1,088	$1,790	$1,849
Feb.	1,043	1,100	1,767	1,680
Mar.	1,158	1,334	1,900	1,888
Apr.	1,094	1,268	1,847	1,894
May	1,174	1,308	1,886	1,780
June	1,228	1,256	1,887	1,850
July	1,046	1,163	1,918	1,903
Aug.	1,100	1,067	1,668	1,740
Sept.	973	1,034	1,635	1,625
Oct.	1,121	1,259	1,909	1,720
Nov.	1,136	1,213	1,849	1,808
Dec.	1,243	1,499	2,261	2,303

Source: Life Insurance Fact Book, 1949. Institute of Life Insurance, New York, N.Y.

Multiple-time Charts

Multiple-time charts provide a means of comparing monthly data on a single item for any number of selected years. The chart, Fig. 3-21, shows the seasonal variation in the purchase of life insurance over a period of specified years.

Comparing Periods of Time

Periods of time may also be compared by using two time scales. Here again, as in the multiple-amount-scale chart (see chart, Fig. 3-18), particular care must be taken to identify the time scale with its corresponding curve.

The chart in Fig. 3-22 compares wholesale prices in two world wars. Note that both time scale and labels relating to World War I are slanted, whereas those concerning World War II are vertical.

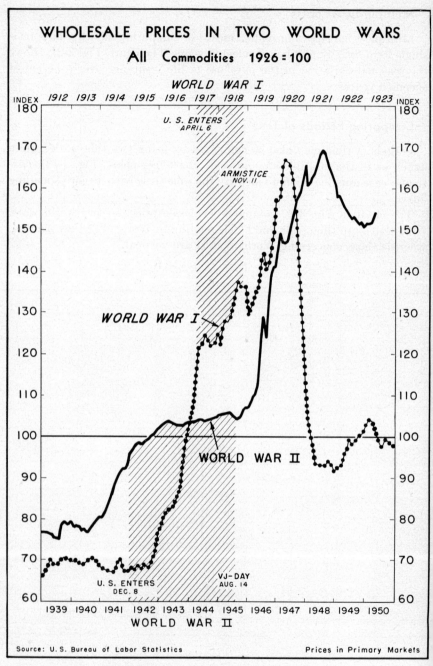

WHOLESALE PRICES IN TWO WORLD WARS
All Commodities 1926 = 100

Source: U.S. Bureau of Labor Statistics   Prices in Primary Markets

Fig. 3-22. Comparing two periods of time.

TABLE 3-12. Wholesale Prices* in Two World Wars
All commodities
Index numbers 1926 = 100
World War I

Months	1912	1913	1914	1915	1916	1917	1918	1919	1920	1921	1922	1923
Jan.	66.0	70.3	68.6	68.1	77.0	102.1	125.0	134.4	157.7	114.0	91.4	102.0
Feb.	66.7	69.8	68.3	68.6	78.5	104.5	122.7	129.8	157.1	104.9	92.9	103.3
Mar.	67.5	69.9	68.0	68.2	80.4	107.7	126.4	131.3	158.6	102.4	92.8	104.5
Apr.	69.7	69.7	67.6	68.7	81.7	114.1	128.3	133.0	165.5	98.9	93.2	103.9
May	70.0	68.9	67.4	69.0	82.5	120.7	128.1	135.3	167.2	96.2	96.1	101.9
June	69.0	69.0	67.4	68.3	82.9	122.0	129.0	135.6	166.5	93.4	96.3	100.3
July	68.9	69.5	67.3	69.3	83.4	123.0	132.0	141.1	165.8	93.4	99.4	98.4
Aug.	69.7	69.7	69.6	68.6	85.1	124.8	134.3	144.3	161.4	93.5	98.6	97.8
Sept.	70.5	70.6	70.2	68.3	86.9	123.5	137.5	141.1	155.2	93.4	99.3	99.7
Oct.	70.8	70.4	68.0	70.2	91.1	122.2	136.3	141.6	144.2	94.1	99.6	99.4
Nov.	70.2	70.1	67.5	71.7	97.4	122.8	136.3	144.5	133.4	94.2	100.5	98.4
Dec.	70.1	69.1	67.3	74.0	99.2	122.9	136.3	150.5	120.7	92.9	100.7	98.1

World War II

Months	1939	1940	1941	1942	1943	1944	1945	1946	1947	1948	1949	1950
Jan.	76.9	79.4	80.8	96.0	101.9	103.3	104.9	107.1	141.5	165.7	160.6	151.5
Feb.	76.9	78.7	80.6	96.7	102.5	103.6	105.2	107.7	144.5	160.9	158.1	152.7
Mar.	76.7	78.4	81.5	97.6	103.4	103.8	105.3	108.9	149.5	161.4	158.4	152.7
Apr.	76.2	78.6	83.2	98.7	103.7	103.9	105.7	110.2	147.7	162.8	156.9	152.9
May	76.2	78.4	84.9	98.8	104.1	104.0	106.0	111.0	147.1	163.9	155.7	155.9
June	75.6	77.5	87.1	98.6	103.8	104.3	106.1	112.9	147.6	166.2	154.5	
July	75.4	77.7	88.8	98.7	103.2	104.1	105.9	124.7	150.6	168.7	153.6	
Aug.	75.0	77.4	90.3	99.2	103.1	103.9	105.7	129.1	153.6	169.5	153.0	
Sept.	79.1	78.0	91.8	99.6	103.1	104.0	105.2	124.0	157.4	168.7	153.6	
Oct.	79.4	78.7	92.4	100.0	103.0	104.1	105.9	134.1	158.5	165.2	152.2	
Nov.	79.2	79.6	92.5	100.3	102.9	104.4	106.8	139.7	159.7	164.0	151.6	
Dec.	79.2	80.0	93.6	101.0	103.2	104.7	107.1	140.9	163.2	162.4	151.9	

* Prices in primary markets.
Source: U.S. Bureau of Labor Statistics.

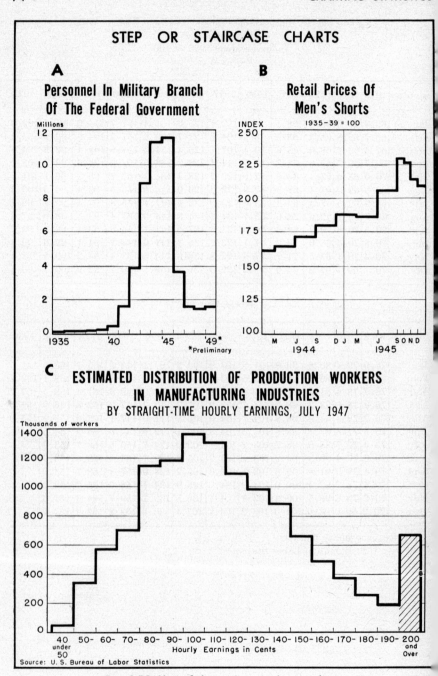

STEP OR STAIRCASE CHARTS

A

Personnel In Military Branch Of The Federal Government

B

Retail Prices Of Men's Shorts

C

ESTIMATED DISTRIBUTION OF PRODUCTION WORKERS IN MANUFACTURING INDUSTRIES
BY STRAIGHT-TIME HOURLY EARNINGS, JULY 1947

Source: U. S. Bureau of Labor Statistics

Fig. 3-23. Use of the step or staircase chart.

Step or Staircase Charts

The step or staircase chart, as shown in the charts, Fig. 3-23, is used to best advantage:

1. *When showing abrupt fluctuations in data.* In chart *A* of Fig. 3-23, the steepness of the trend showing personnel in the military branch would be impossible to read as a curve chart.

2. *When presenting irregular periods of time.* In chart *B*, the same price is carried over from plotted date to date. A curve connecting the two points would result in a slope that would suggest that the rise had been gradual, whereas the step shows exactly the extent of time the quotation covers.

3. *When depicting frequency distribution.* In chart *C*, the relative size of the class intervals is quickly evident. The shading of the last group calls attention to the fact that that interval includes more than 200 workers.

Common practice in presenting a frequency-distribution step chart is to break the horizontal scale. The extreme limits are grouped and the complete extent of the distribution is not usually shown.

The horizontal scale on the step chart may show size, number, class interval, location, or time. As a rule, only one series of data is plotted, because the vertical rulings of the steps may coincide and more than one line would be confusing. The chart in Fig. 3-24 illustrates this difficulty. The salary rates for the different fields of engineering are hard to follow.

The same data plotted as a line in the chart in Fig. 3-25 show the trend of salary rates but do not so emphatically distinguish the years of experience.

Shading or crosshatching the surface of the step chart, as in Fig. 3-26, further accents the general trend. The first and last intervals were given heavier shading in order to call special attention to the fact that the end intervals, those receiving under 60 cents and over \$1.80 per hour, were grouped.

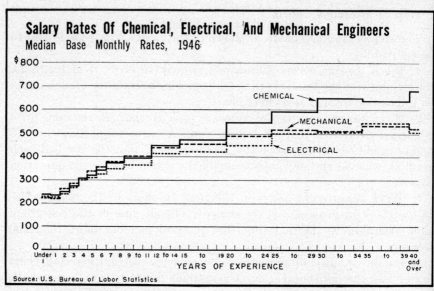

Fig. 3-24. Two or more series on step chart are confusing.

TABLE 3-13. MEDIAN BASE MONTHLY SALARY RATES OF ENGINEERS, BY YEARS OF EXPERIENCE, 1946

Years of experience	Chemical	Mechanical	Electrical	Plotting points,* years
Less than 1	$242	$226	$228	$\frac{1}{2}$
1	241	225	237	1
2	255	264	249	2
3	278	285	277	3
4	310	308	303	4
5	327	342	315	5
6	344	360	325	6
7–8	375	380	347	8
9–11	399	408	366	$10\frac{1}{2}$
12–14	452	442	409	$13\frac{1}{2}$
15–19	474	455	418	$17\frac{1}{2}$
20–24	552	492	454	$22\frac{1}{2}$
25–29	598	518	502	$27\frac{1}{2}$
30–34	655	514	513	$32\frac{1}{2}$
35–39	640	534	545	$37\frac{1}{2}$
40 and over	680	520	509	40

Source: U.S. Bureau of Labor Statistics.

* For Fig. 3-25.

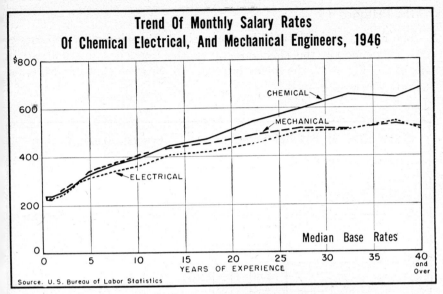

Fig. 3-25. The curves show the trend of frequency rates.

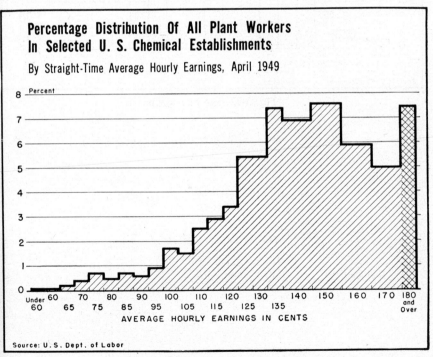

Fig. 3-26. Shading the step chart.

The Histogram

The histogram is plotted like a step chart. Its columnlike appearance sharply delineates the class interval of the frequency distribution. In the chart, Fig. 3-27, the salary intervals are clearly defined and the distribution is easy to read.

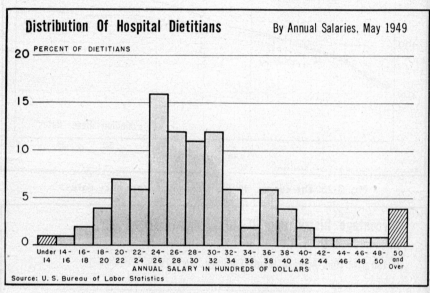

Fig. 3-27. The histogram.

The Cumulative Curve

The cumulative curve is used when the primary interest is in the cumulated picture for an extended period of time. This cumulation of data tends to smooth the fluctuations of the curve. The chart, Fig. 3-28, shows the cumulated number of new permanent nonfarm dwelling units started from 1920 through 1948.

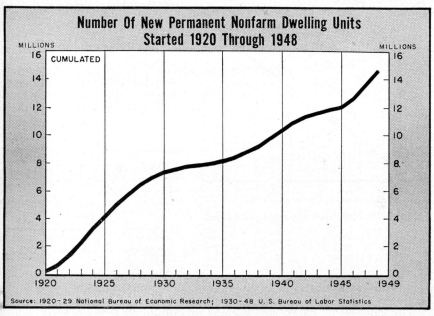

Fig 3-28. The cumulated curve chart.

In preparing the table for the drafting room to use when plotting, addition of data from period to period should be computed and not left to the responsibility of the draftsman. The chart, Fig. 3-29, was plotted by the draftsman from the cumulated Table 3-14.

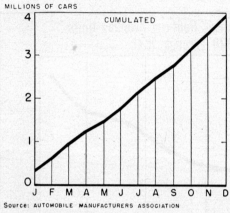

FACTORY SALES OF PASSENGER CARS
FOR THE YEAR 1948

Fig. 3-29. Plot from a cumulated table.

TABLE 3-14. FACTORY SALES OF PASSENGER CARS FOR YEAR 1948		
		Cumulated for use by draftsman
Jan.	305,081	305,081
Feb.	274,847	579,928
Mar.	349,998	929,926
Apr.	308,071	1,237,997
May	225,461	1,463,458
June	312,406	1,775,864
July	356,764	2,132,628
Aug.	348,822	2,481,450
Sept.	301,170	2,782,620
Oct.	383,755	3,166,375
Nov.	364,440	3,530,815
Dec.	378,455	3,909,270

Source: Auto Facts, 1949. Automobile Manufacturers Association, Detroit, Mich.

A Progress Report

The cumulative curve also has the advantage of being able to show progress toward a goal. For example, a corporation has contracted to deliver 7,250 planes from July, 1940, to July, 1942, to two different destinations or zones. The upper chart, Fig. 3-30, shows the cumulated deliveries plotted, along with the number scheduled to be delivered. The lower chart uses the subdivided connected column to show the number of monthly deliveries to each of the two zones. Thus the monthly progress is clearly pictured, as well as the cumulated production in relation to the ultimate goal.

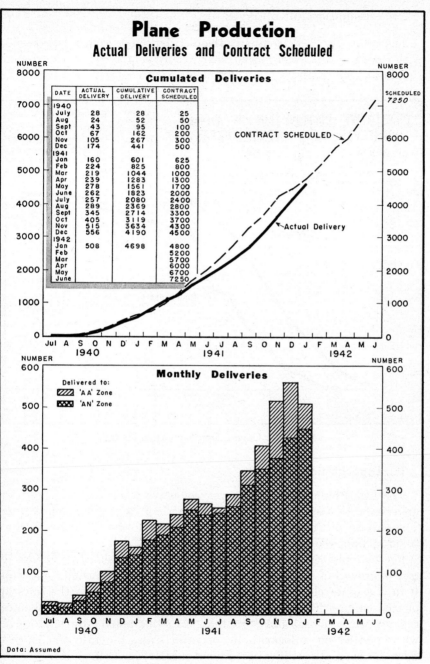

Plane Production
Actual Deliveries and Contract Scheduled

NUMBER   NUMBER

Cumulated Deliveries

DATE	ACTUAL DELIVERY	CUMULATIVE DELIVERY	CONTRACT SCHEDULED
1940			
July	28	28	25
Aug	24	52	50
Sept	43	95	100
Oct	67	162	200
Nov	105	267	300
Dec	174	441	500
1941			
Jan	160	601	625
Feb	224	825	800
Mar	219	1044	1000
Apr	239	1283	1300
May	278	1561	1700
June	262	1823	2000
July	257	2080	2400
Aug	289	2369	2800
Sept	345	2714	3300
Oct	405	3119	3700
Nov	515	3634	4300
Dec	556	4190	4500
1942			
Jan	508	4698	4800
Feb			5200
Mar			5700
Apr			6000
May			6700
June			7250

SCHEDULED 7250

CONTRACT SCHEDULED

Actual Delivery

Jul A S O N D J F M A M J J A S O N D J F M A M J
    1940   1941   1942

Monthly Deliveries

NUMBER   NUMBER

Delivered to:
 'AA' Zone
 'AN' Zone

Jul A S O N D J F M A M J J A S O N D J F M A M J
    1940   1941   1942

Data: Assumed

Fig. 3-30. A progress report.

Comparing Cumulative Curves

The chart, Fig. 3-31, compares the distribution of women bookkeepers with stenographers according to their weekly salaries. This type of chart should be used sparingly, as it is difficult to understand.

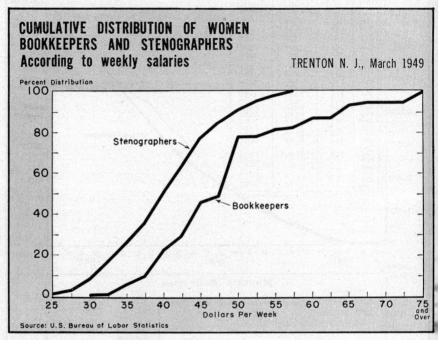

Fig. 3-31. Comparing cumulative curves.

The Logarithmic Chart

The logarithmic chart, while very effective when properly used and understood by the reader, is not for indiscriminate popular presentation. The purpose of this type of chart is to show the rate of change within a trend and not the arithmetic amount of change.

For example, let us assume that a chain store wishes to compare the rate of growth of sales in two stores. Store A is in a large city and Store B in a new development. In the charts, Fig. 3-32, when the sales are plotted on an arithmetic scale, Store A's sales appear to have advanced rapidly, while the sales in Store B appear as a gradual growth. However, when plotted on a logarithmic or ratio scale, the rate of change of sales shows an almost identical rate of increase for both stores.

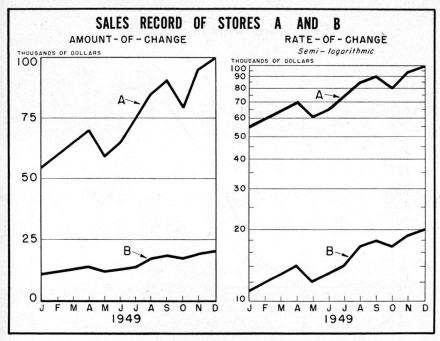

Fig. 3-32. Comparing arithmetic and logarithmic scales.

TABLE 3-15. Sales Record

	Store A	Store B
Jan.	$55,000	$11,000
Feb.	60,000	12,000
Mar.	65,000	13,000
Apr.	70,000	14,000
May	60,000	12,000
June	65,000	13,000
July	75,000	14,000
Aug.	85,000	16,500
Sept.	90,000	18,000
Oct.	80,000	16,500
Nov.	95,000	19,000
Dec.	100,000	20,000

Data assumed.

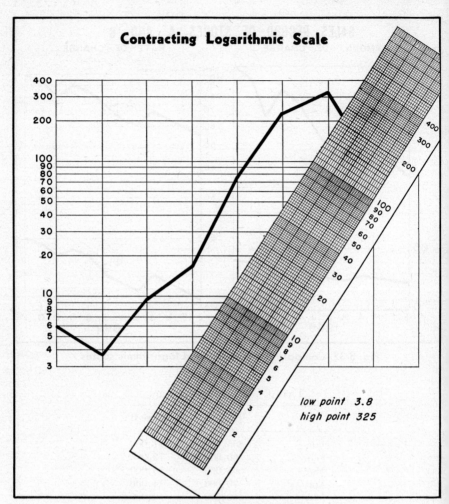

Fig. 3-33. Constructing grid for a logarithmic chart.

Logarithmic Grids

The grid with the vertical ruling carrying the logarithmic scale and the horizontal ruling carrying the arithmetic scale denoting time is the most common. The reverse may be used, and the horizontal ruling may carry the log scale. Charts of this type are frequently referred to as "semilog charts." In this text the term "logarithmic" means the same as semilogarithmic and is used interchangeably.

The full or double log scale (with the log grid carried on both horizontal and vertical rulings) is used mostly for statistical study and economic analysis and is not a good tool for popular presentation of data. Because of its infrequent use, no example is given.

Reading a Log Scale

This visual difference in trend is due to the fact that in the graph with the arithmetic scale the amounts are read from the zero base line, whereas points plotted on a semilogarithmic chart are read from point to point, rather than from a base line, because there is *no zero* on a logarithmic scale.

To read the curves correctly on the logarithmic chart, it must be understood that the steepness or slope of the lines connecting the plotted points indicates the rate of change. That is, the steeper the rise or fall of these lines, the greater the ratio of increase or decrease from point to point.

Constructing a Log Chart

When making logarithmic charts, it is not necessary to convert an arithmetic scale into logarithms; semilogarithmic and full logarithmic printed sheets are obtainable from art and drafting supply stores and arithmetic data may be plotted directly on them. Or if it is desired to construct a semilog grid by line extension, use a printed logarithmic grid as a guide, as shown in Fig. 3-33.

Figure 3-34 shows how to construct one cycle of a log scale which will fit into a given space. This guide may also be used for marking off a plotting scale to facilitate plotting of trends.

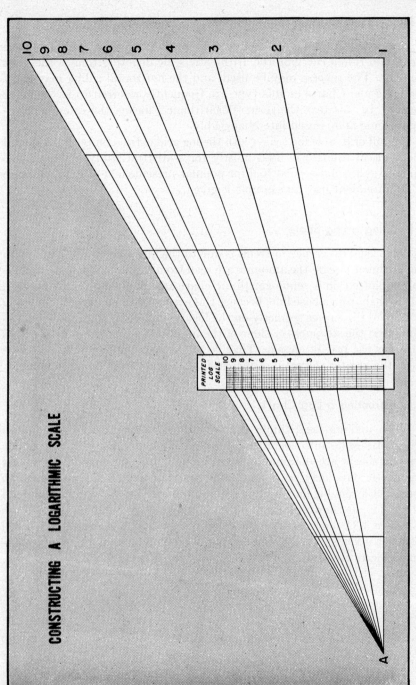

Fig. 3-34. Making a log scale by line extension.

Selecting the Scale Unit

The logarithmic scale may consist of several cycles (decks, spans, or phases) beginning with any number greater than zero. The value placed at the top of the cycle will be ten times that at the bottom of the cycle. Figure 3-35 shows a few selected scales.

If the complete data do not warrant a full cycle, part of the grid may be drawn—that is enough to accommodate the high and low points. The chart, Fig. 3-36, required two whole cycles and part of a third to show the trends in the rate of growth of petroleum production and crude reserves.

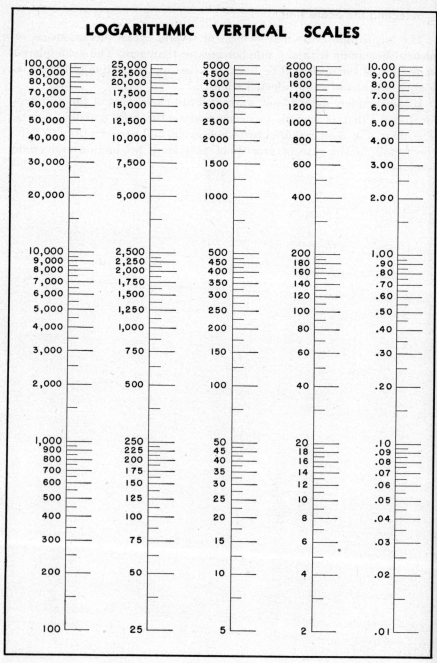

Fig. 3-35. Selected logarithmic scale units.

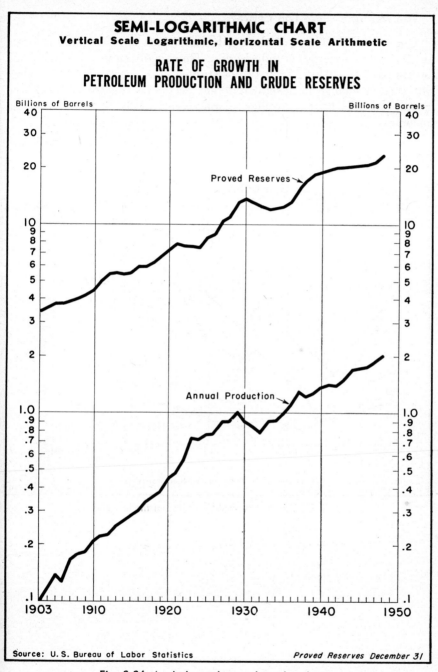

SEMI-LOGARITHMIC CHART
Vertical Scale Logarithmic, Horizontal Scale Arithmetic

RATE OF GROWTH IN
PETROLEUM PRODUCTION AND CRUDE RESERVES

Fig. 3-36. A whole cycle need not be shown.

The Multiple-curve Log Chart

One of the chief uses of the logarithmic chart is to compare the rate of change of categories of unlike units. Thus, many curves can be plotted on the same graph and their trends studied. The chart, Fig. 3-37, shows the rate of change in several different economic trends in the United States, such as hours, earnings, employment, production, and national income.

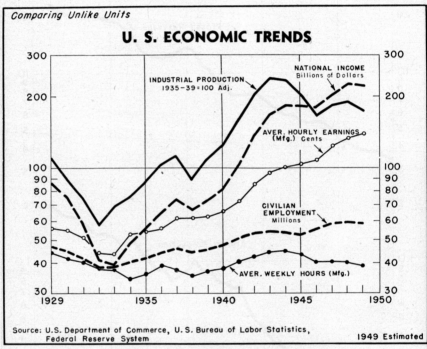

Fig. 3-37. Comparing unlike units on the log chart.

When Not to Use the Log Chart

The semilogarithmic chart should *not* be used:

1. *For the purpose of bringing two curves of a widely different magnitude together in order to compare their amounts more closely.* This is a common error. The log chart would still show the rate of change and not the amount of change. Both of the charts in Fig. 3-38 are correct for their purposes, but each shows a different aspect of the same data.

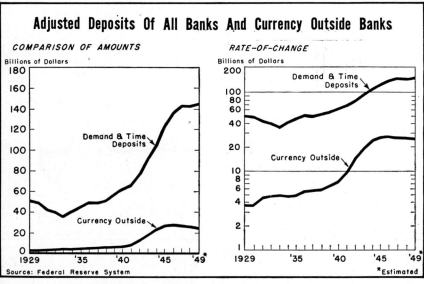

Fig. 3-38. The logarithmic chart shows rate of change.

2. *To enlarge the "flat" portion in a trend.* Rather, insert a small chart to show detail (see chart *A*, Fig. 3-39).

3. *To show both negative and positive values in a series.* Of course, there are no negative values on a log scale. The arithmetic scale will show these amount differences (see chart *B*, Fig. 3-39).

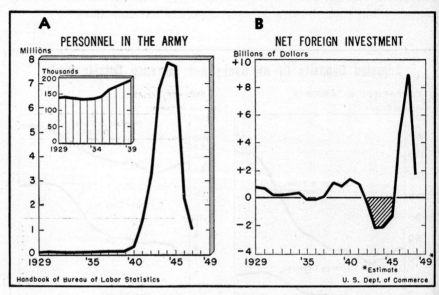

Fig. 3-39. When not to plot on a log scale.

The Fan Chart

The fan chart may be used to show either the percentage of change or the index increase or decrease of items from one selected base date to another period of time. This form of chart has the advantage over a table in that the amount of change is visually shown in numerical order. The chart, Fig. 3-40, shows the percentage loss or gain in newsstand sales of leading magazines. The background shading accents the spread of the percentage of change.

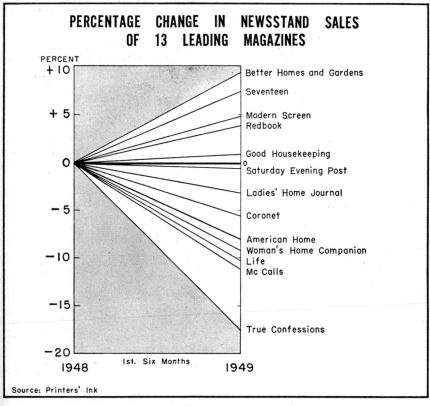

Fig. 3-40. Shading the fan chart.

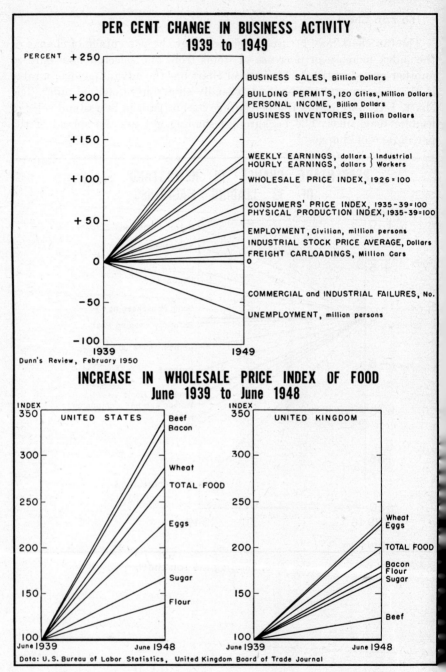

PER CENT CHANGE IN BUSINESS ACTIVITY
1939 to 1949

PERCENT +250

BUSINESS SALES, Billion Dollars

+200
BUILDING PERMITS, 120 Cities, Million Dollars
PERSONAL INCOME, Billion Dollars
BUSINESS INVENTORIES, Billion Dollars

+150

WEEKLY EARNINGS, dollars } Industrial
HOURLY EARNINGS, dollars } Workers
+100
WHOLESALE PRICE INDEX, 1926 = 100

CONSUMERS' PRICE INDEX, 1935-39=100
PHYSICAL PRODUCTION INDEX, 1935-39=100
+50
EMPLOYMENT, Civilian, million persons
INDUSTRIAL STOCK PRICE AVERAGE, Dollars
FREIGHT CARLOADINGS, Million Cars
0   0

COMMERCIAL and INDUSTRIAL FAILURES, No.
-50
UNEMPLOYMENT, million persons

-100
1939   1949

Dunn's Review, February 1950

INCREASE IN WHOLESALE PRICE INDEX OF FOOD
June 1939 to June 1948

INDEX   INDEX
350   UNITED STATES   Beef   350   UNITED KINGDOM
                          Bacon

300   300

                          Wheat
                          TOTAL FOOD
250   250
                                                                    Wheat
                          Eggs   Eggs
200   200
                                                                    TOTAL FOOD
                                                                    Bacon
                          Sugar   Flour
150   150   Sugar

                          Flour
                                                                    Beef
100   100
June 1939   June 1948   June 1939   June 1948

Data: U.S. Bureau of Labor Statistics, United Kingdom Board of Trade Journal

Fig. 3-41. The fan chart shows comparisons in numerical order.

The fan chart at the top of Fig. 3-41 depicts the percentage of change in business activity over ten years. Business sales rose remarkably and unemployment dropped.

The rise in food prices in the United States and in the United Kingdom is shown in the two lower charts. A closer comparison could be made by using the United States chart as a base and making an acetate overlay in color of the United Kingdom (see overlay, Fig. 1-8).

4 • THE SURFACE CHART

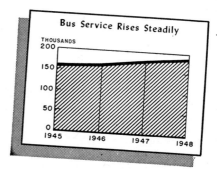

TABLE	School	Local	Intercity	Other	Total
1943	77.9	45.6	28.5	2.0	154.0
1944	75.5	48.5	28.0	3.3	155.3
1945	83.2	46.0	29.0	1.0	159.2
1946	82.5	47.8	30.3	1.5	162.0
1947	85.9	54.1	31.9	3.0	174.9
1948	90.4	57.2	31.8	3.2	182.6

REVENUE MOTOR BUSES and SCHOOL BUSES

IN THOUSANDS · EST

Source. Automobile Facts and Figures

The surface chart is sometimes called the "band," "strata," or "layer cake." It should be used:

1. *When the magnitude of a trend is to be emphasized, as in a simple surface chart.*

2. *When the relative importance of components of a total trend over a period of time is to be shown, as in a subdivided-surface chart.*

3. *When some particular portion of the trend is to be emphasized, as in a surface zone chart.*

The Simple Surface Chart

The simple surface chart depicts a single trend. Its layout and plotting are similar to those of a line chart. Shading, crosshatching, photographs, or illustrations are used to fill in the area below the trend line. This shading, as in the chart in Fig. 4-1, tends to give a silhouette effect which emphasizes the over-all picture of the trend.

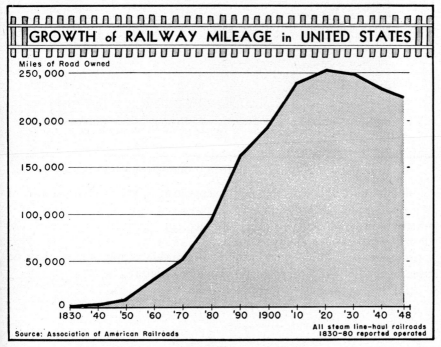

Fig. 4-1. The simple surface chart.

99

Photosurface

In the chart, Fig. 4-2, a cutout photograph serves as a shading. The chart was first completed and inked in. The trend, base line, and connecting vertical grids were traced on transparent paper. The tracing was then laid over the photograph. The portion to be used was marked, cut out, and applied to the chart with rubber cement.

Fig. 4-2. Use of the photosurface (Courtesy of Albert Spear).

In this particular case the chart was scaled to fit the selected area of the photograph. At times it may be necessary to enlarge or reduce the photograph in order to cover the surface below the trend line with the desired portion of the picture.

Photomount, obtained at most photographic supply stores, may be used instead of rubber cement for mounting pictures.

Acetate Overlay

Another method for obtaining the photosurface chart is to cut the picture to the shape of the trend and mount it on bristolboard. The trend line can then be drawn, in color if desired, on an acetate overlay and placed over the mounted picture (see acetate overlay, Fig. 1-8). This method is effective for exhibits, as it gives both color and animation to the chart.

Optical Illusions

Avoid using black to silhouette a trend, as it causes an optical illusion (unless, of course, it is desired to create an illusion). Part *A* in Fig. 4-3 emphasizes the trend by using black below the trend line, whereas the black shading in part *B*, above the same trend line, seems to reduce the amount of the plottings. The same illusion is created when deep colors are used on original or reproduced charts.

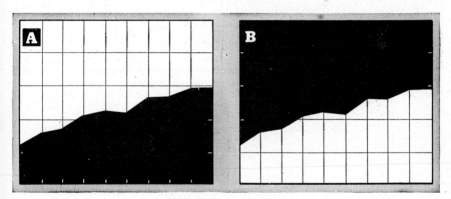

Fig. 4-3. Optical illusions.

The Zero Line

The surface chart should always be plotted from the zero line, as the broken amount scale distorts the picture and overemphasizes the difference in amounts (see chart, Fig. 4-4).

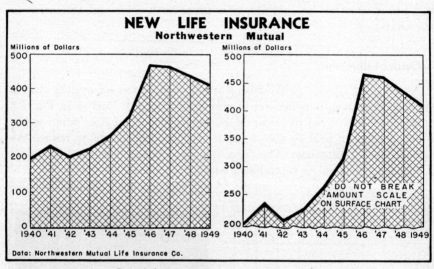

Fig. 4-4. Do not break amount scales.

Plotting on the Vertical Grid

Ticks indicating both the vertical and horizontal scales should be very distinct on a surface chart. It is advisable to start the plotting on the first vertical ruling. A space at the beginning of the plotted trend may be confusing when the time scale is read. This is particularly noticeable in monthly plotting. In this case the first month plotted, whether January or some other month, should be properly identified (see Fig. 4-5A). It is also advisable to rule the last vertical grid to represent the month of December. Although this will make the last year (division span) slightly narrower, it will avoid the appearance of the chart's not being up to date at the end of the year.

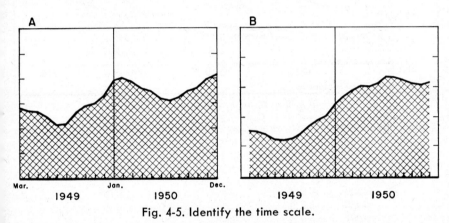

Fig. 4-5. Identify the time scale.

In Fig. 4-5 both trends begin in March, 1949, and end in December, 1950. Part A is correctly labeled, whereas in part B the lack of labels and spaces at either end of grid makes it difficult to identify the months of the first and last plottings.

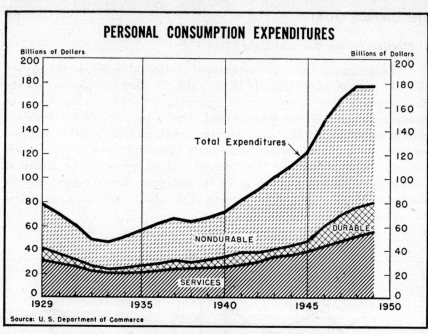

Fig. 4-6. Plotting the band chart.

TABLE 4-1A. PERSONAL CONSUMPTION EXPENDITURES (BILLIONS OF DOLLARS)

	Durable goods	Nondurable goods	Services	Total expenditures
1929	$ 9.4	$ 37.7	$31.7	$ 78.8
1930	7.3	34.1	29.5	70.8
1931	5.6	29.0	26.6	61.2
1932	3.7	22.7	22.8	49.2
1933	3.5	22.3	20.6	46.3
1934	4.3	26.7	20.9	51.9
1935	5.2	29.4	21.7	56.2
1936	6.4	32.9	23.3	62.5
1937	7.0	35.2	24.9	67.1
1938	5.8	34.0	24.7	64.5
1939	6.7	35.3	25.5	67.5
1940	7.9	37.6	26.6	72.1
1941	9.8	44.0	28.5	82.3
1942	7.1	52.9	31.2	91.2
1943	6.8	61.0	34.4	102.2
1944	7.1	67.1	37.4	111.6
1945	8.5	74.9	39.7	123.1
1946	16.5	86.8	44.5	147.8
1947	22.0	96.2	48.8	166.9
1948	23.5	102.2	53.1	178.8
1949	24.8	97.7	56.0	178.5

Source: U.S. Department of Commerce.

104

The Subdivided Surface

The subdivided-surface chart (Fig. 4-6) is a series of bands or strata showing the cumulated components of a total trend. The width of each band is read from the plotted trend below it. This type of chart gives only a general picture and should not be used when changes in the movement of trends are abrupt or when accurate reading of a component is of paramount importance.

For plotting the subdivided-surface chart, it is desirable to prepare a special table for the drafting room. The amounts on this table should be added in proper sequence for plotting. Such a table should be labeled "for plotting only." Compare Tables 4-1A and 4-1B.

TABLE 4-1B. PERSONAL CONSUMPTION EXPENDITURES (BILLIONS OF DOLLARS)
Table to be used only for plotting

	Services +	Durable goods +	Nondurable goods =	Total ex-penditures
1929	$31.7	$41.1		$ 78.8
1930	29.5	36.8		70.8
1931	26.6	32.2		61.2
1932	22.8	26.5		49.2
1933	20.6	24.1		46.3
1934	20.9	25.2		51.9
1935	21.7	26.9		56.2
1936	23.3	29.7		62.5
1937	24.9	31.9		67.1
1938	24.7	30.5		64.5
1939	25.5	32.2		67.5
1940	26.6	34.5		72.1
1941	28.5	38.3		82.3
1942	31.2	38.3		91.2
1943	34.4	41.2		102.2
1944	37.4	44.5		111.6
1945	39.7	48.2		123.1
1946	44.5	61.0		147.8
1947	48.8	70.8		166.9
1948	53.1	76.6		178.8
1949	56.0	80.8		178.5

Sequence of Strata

Because the smoothest trend should be plotted next to the base line, "Services" was used as the first stratum in the chart, Fig. 4-6, and listed as the first column in Table 4-1B. The next smoothest trend, "Durable Goods," is added to "Services," and this sum is set up as column 2 on the table.

"Nondurable Goods" (the third area) makes up the difference between the first two components and the total. Therefore the total becomes the third plotting. Using the cumulated table and plotting each trend from the base line is much more accurate than following the original table and plotting by means of an auxiliary scale. The reason for this is that, no matter how carefully the trends are plotted above each other, slight errors add up, and the final plotting will not check with the total trend line.

Choosing the proper sequence in plotting the bands of this type of chart is of major importance. To help make this choice it is practical to plot the curves first on printed crosshatched paper. In this way the character of the trends may be studied and the curves with the least movement may be plotted in ascending sequence (see chart in Fig. 4-7).

WORK SHEET.

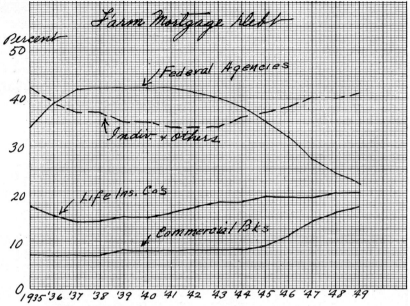

Fig. 4-7. Study the movement of trends.

The 100 Per Cent Surface Chart

The 100 per cent surface or band chart (Fig. 4-8) shows the changing trend in distribution of farm mortgage debt. Keeping the strata in order of least disturbance avoids distortion and optical illusion, which make the bands difficult to read.

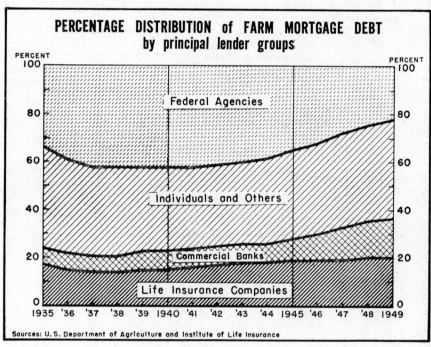

Fig. 4-8. The 100 per cent surface chart.

In the first half of the chart in Fig. 4-9, it can readily be seen that the movement of the bottom band is reflected in those above it. This makes it almost impossible visually to judge the width of the band on the steep slopes. There is a positive tendency to read the amount on the slant rather than in a vertical direction.

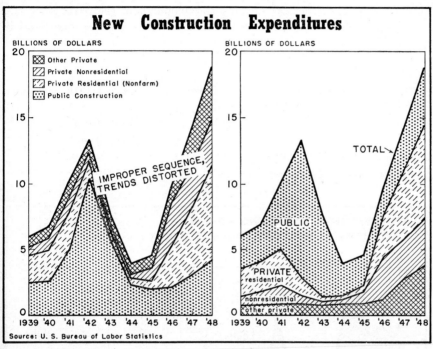

Fig. 4-9. The band with the least movement should be plotted first.

The second part of this chart shows a better sequence in plotting and still maintains the proper division of "Public" and "Private" expenditures. The difference is also made stronger by using dots for "Public" and line patterns for "Private." However, this same data plotted as a subdivided or component column would show an even more comprehensive picture (see Fig. 5-10).

Note also in the chart in Fig. 4-9 that there is a breakdown within the "Private" subtotal group. These must be kept together as a unit and separate from "Public," even though it might be necessary to break the rule of the smoothest curve sequence.

Labeling and Shading Strata

When identifying the bands or strata, label directly in the band if possible. If the surface is too narrow, carry a legend in the part of the chart that is best suited for the purpose. The outline of the total trend will determine this space.

As a rule in shading a band chart, tone from dark at the bottom to lightest pattern at the top, keeping the diagonals of the patterns in the same general direction (see chart, Fig. 2-12). If, however, one band is of special interest, make that one darkest in shade or in the most striking pattern. Make crosshatching distinctive in pattern and contrasting in tonal quality.

Above all, keep in mind that the fewer the bands or strata, the more easily the over-all story may be read.

The shaded surface chart may also be used to point up a story more definitely. While the data in the chart, Fig. 4-10, may be drawn as two trend lines, a greater contrast is brought out by the use of the white "Lay-off" curve against the surface of the "Quit" trend.

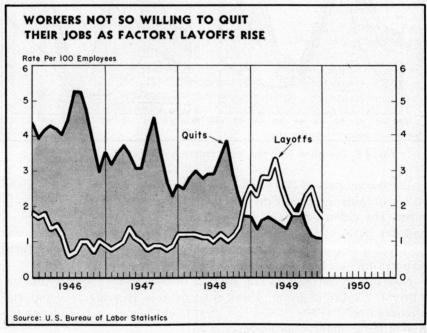

Fig. 4-10. A curve superimposed on a surface.

Shaded Zone Charts

In the zone chart, differences may be stressed by shading the area or zone between the two trends. The chart, Fig. 4-11, emphasizes the growth of two-or-more family dwelling units started in Washington, D.C., from the last of 1947 through 1949.

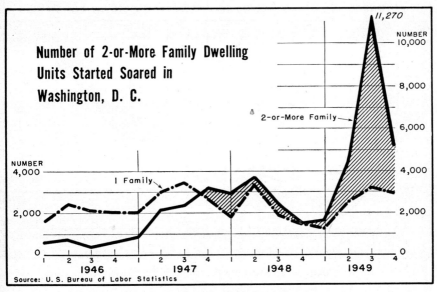

Fig. 4-11. The shaded zone chart.

The shaded zone in the chart, Fig. 4-12 is of particular significance, showing the gain in prices received by farmers over prices paid from 1942 through 1949.

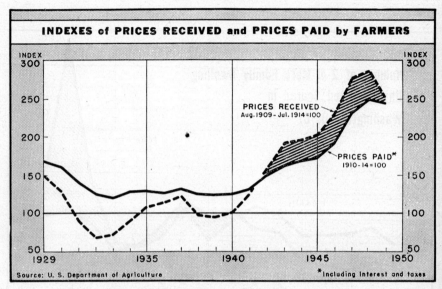

Fig. 4-12. Shading sharpens differences.

In showing the difference between two curves representing a balance of gains and losses, or income and expenditure, two different shading patterns may be used. This method is effective in showing reversals over a period of time.

The chart, Fig. 4-13, shows the rise and fall of life insurance ownership per family for three decades. Of particular interest is the stability of the life insurance trend during the thirties.

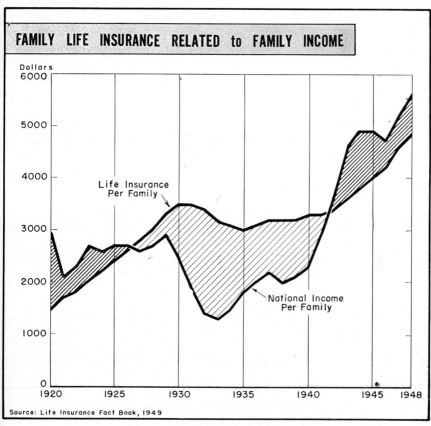

Fig. 4-13. Use of two shadings.

5 • COLUMN CHARTS

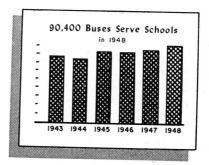

TABLE	REVENUE MOTOR BUSES and SCHOOL BUSES				
	School	Local	Intercity	Other	Total
1943	77.9	45.6	28.5	2.0	154.0
1944	75.5	48.5	28.0	3.3	155.3
1945	83.2	46.0	29.0	1.0	159.2
1946	82.5	47.8	30.3	1.5	162.0
1947	85.9	54.1	31.9	3.0	174.9
1948	90.4	57.2	31.8	3.2	182.6

IN THOUSANDS   EST.

Source: Automobile Facts and Figures

90,400 Buses Serve Schools
in 1948

1943 1944 1945 1946 1947 1948

The column chart is sometimes referred to as the "vertical bar." Its primary purpose is to depict numerical values of a given item over a period of time (see Table 5-1). These values, either absolute or per cent, are represented by the height of the column.

In the chart, Fig. 5-1, the given item—"Workers Employed by Construction Contractors"—is for a period of ten years.

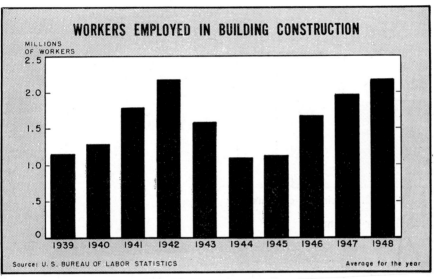

WORKERS EMPLOYED IN BUILDING CONSTRUCTION

Source: U. S. BUREAU OF LABOR STATISTICS   Average for the year

Fig. 5-1. The column chart.

TABLE 5-1. Workers Employed by Construction Contractors (Thousands)

1939	1,150.2	1944	1,093.8
1940	1,293.5	1945	1,132.3
1941	1,789.6	1946	1,660.6
1942	2,169.5	1947	1,982.1
1943	1,566.6	1948	2,165.0

Source: U.S. Bureau of Labor Statistics.

The column chart is preferable to the curve chart when a sharper delineation of trend is to be shown. Laid out in proper proportion with a plan for the design of the chart as a whole, the column chart is a more dramatic presentation for public display.

Layout of Columns

The layout and design of the standard statistical column chart require special care as to spacing and width of column. Although the dimensions of the printed page, or space allotted in an exhibit, control the layout to a certain extent, good proportions in spacing should be carried out. If the space between the columns is approximately one-half the width of the column, the layout will be in balance.

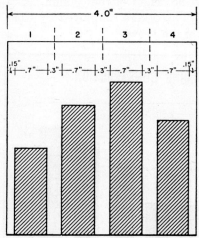

Example:

Given—horizontal grid space of 4 inches.

To lay out four columns.

Divide given space into four parts.

A balanced division of this space is:
Column .7 inch wide.
Space between columns .3 inch.
Leaving .15-inch space between grid and end columns.

(See Fig. 5-2.)

Fig. 5-2. Spacing of columns.

Grid for Columns

Usually only the horizontal grid is necessary, but this grid may be eliminated and ticks substituted if a more general reading is adequate. When inking in, both amount-scale ticks and base lines are made heavier in weight than those in the line chart to allow for the more solid appearance of the columns (see Fig. 5-15 for exception).

Numerals in Columns

When only a few columns are plotted, it is feasible to drop the amount scale and to letter in the actual amounts (see chart, Fig. 5-3). If this is done, the figures should be inserted within the columns near the top. Placing them outside and above the columns tends to exaggerate the height and interferes with a clear comparison of the columns.

WORK STOPPAGES
Involving 10,000 or more workers

29 · 31 · 11 · 15 · 20 · 18

1935-39 · 1941 · 1946 · 1947 · 1948 · 1949

Data: U.S. Bureau of Labor Statistics · Selected periods

Fig. 5-3. Placing numerals in columns.

Breaking Amount Scale

As in the surface chart, the amount scale should *not* be broken when a complete comparison of data is to be shown. If, however, in the data to be presented there is one erratic point that is not significant in the general trend, this column may be broken at the top and the amount shown directly above it. Breaking the erratic column in Fig. 5-4 does not obscure the purpose of the chart.

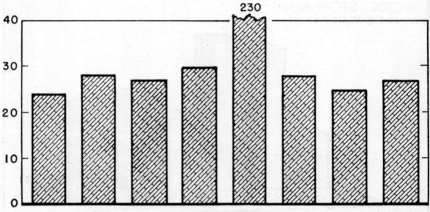

Fig. 5-4. Breaking the column for an erratic plotting.

Irregular Time Sequence

When a few irregularities occur in the time sequence of a fairly long period, space should be allowed on the time scale for the width of the missing columns (see Fig. 5-5).

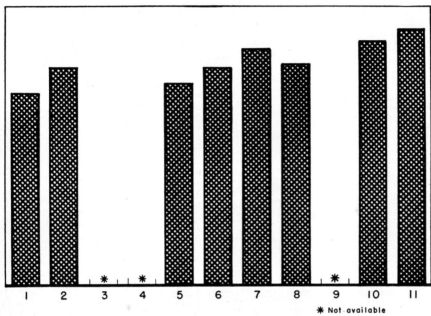

Fig. 5-5. Allow width of column for missing data.

Selected Dates

If the chart is made up of selected dates of either regular or irregular incidence (Fig. 5-6), the space between the columns should be uniform and the dates lettered clearly below them.

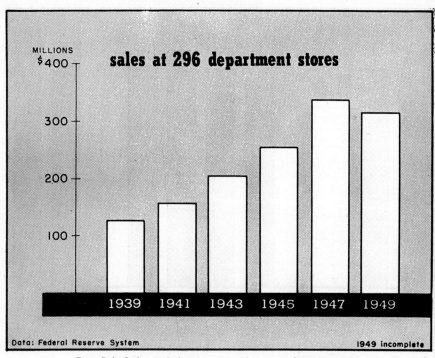

Fig. 5-6. Selected dates spaced at regular intervals.

Grouped Columns

The grouped-column chart is used to compare two, or sometimes three, independent series over a period of time (see Fig. 5-7). Contrasting shading or coloring will set off the columns and show effectively their differences in amount. A legend or key is necessary to identify the category of each column. Ordinarily the key should be placed in the upper left-hand corner of the grid, but lack of space may require that it appear as a subtitle, or even at the bottom of the chart.

Multiple-amount scales are to be avoided on a grouped-column chart because of the confusion of linking the key with its corresponding scale and column. When two categories are to be plotted, necessitating two scales, a paired-bar chart (see Fig. 6-17) should be made.

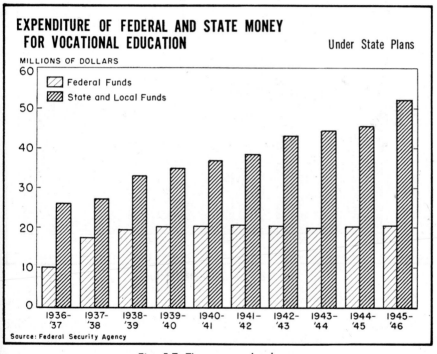

Fig. 5-7. The grouped column.

Connected Columns

The connected-column chart shows effectively the over-all picture for a long period of time. Connected as in the chart, Fig. 5-8, it accents the time element as well as the whole trend. This type of graph is usually necessary when spaced columns would appear crowded.

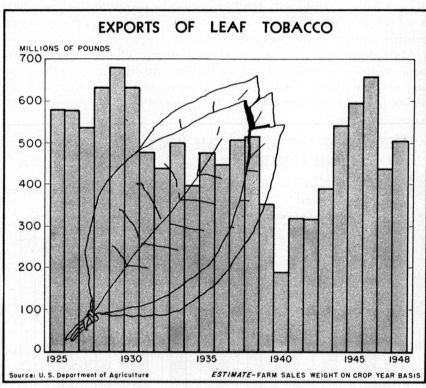

Fig. 5-8. The connected column.

Subdivided Column

The charts in Fig. 5-9 illustrate the difference in layout between a line chart and a column chart. Both are made from the same data. While the line chart may be plotted directly from the original table, it is best for the sake of accuracy to cumulate a special table for the plotting of the subdivided column (see Table 5-2).

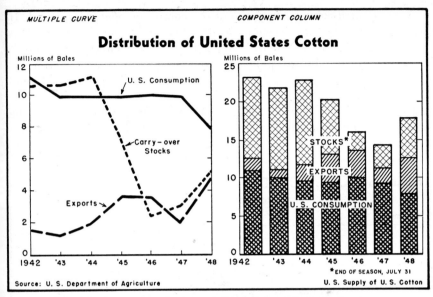

Fig. 5-9. Comparing the line chart and the subdivided column.

TABLE 5-2. DISTRIBUTION OF UNITED STATES COTTON, JULY 31 (MILLIONS OF BALES)

	Mill consumption	Exports	Stocks (end of season)	Total supply
1942	11,160	1,480	10,657	23,297
1943	9,993	1,139	10,744	21,876
1944	9,693	2,007	11,164	22,864
1945	9,423	3,613	7,326	20,362
1946	10,072	3,545	2,530	16,147
1947	9,374	1,968	3,080	14,422
1948	7,833	4,785	5,283	17,901

DATA FOR PLOTTING COMPONENT-COLUMN CHART

	Mill consumption	+ Exports + Stocks	= Total supply
1942	11,160	12,640	23,297
1943	9,993	11,132	21,876
1944	9,693	11,700	22,864
1945	9,423	13,036	20,362
1946	10,072	13,617	16,147
1947	9,374	11,342	14,422
1948	7,833	12,618	17,901

Source: U.S. Department of Agriculture.

A subdivided-column chart shows the component parts of a total. It is similar in purpose to the subdivided-surface chart, but the fluctuations of the segments are more sharply defined. These segments or components should be few in number, and each should carry a distinctive pattern so that it may be readily identified. For this identification, a key or legend is necessary.

However, since the chart, Fig. 5-10, has only two components, the customary key is not important. The plotted surface, which is plainly labeled, can be easily identified.

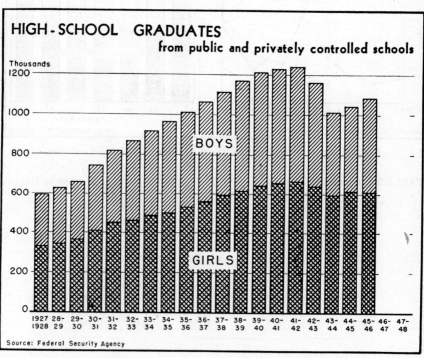

Fig. 5-10. Labeling the components directly is possible here.

The chart, Fig. 5-11, must carry a key or legend because of the number of components and the irregularity of their plotted amounts. Because this chart is three-dimensional, the scale is carried only on the left-hand grid.

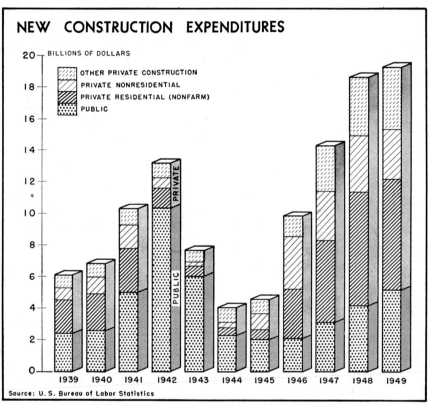

Fig. 5-11. A key is necessary for these subdivided columns.

Deviation Column

The deviation column provides a method for plotting positive and negative data over a period of time, that is, increases and decreases, losses and gains, or deviation from a requirement or norm. The chart, Fig. 5-12, shows the net change in dollars in business inventories from year to year.

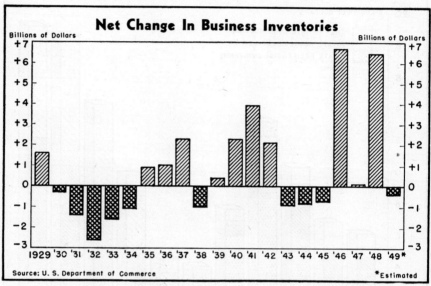

Fig. 5-12. Deviation columns.

TABLE 5-3. NET CHANGE IN BUSINESS INVENTORIES (BILLIONS OF DOLLARS)

1929	$ 1.6	1936	$ 1.0	1943	$−0.9
1930	−0.3	1937	2.3	1944	−0.8
1931	−1.4	1938	−1.0	1945	−0.7
1932	−2.6	1939	0.4	1946	6.7
1933	−1.6	1940	2.3	1947	0.1
1934	−1.1	1941	3.9	1948	6.5
1935	0.9	1942	2.1	1949	−0.4

Source: U.S. Department of Commerce.

In a deviation-column chart, each column is either positive or negative —never both. In this type of chart, a column representing either a per cent or an absolute number is plotted above the base line for a positive amount or below the base line for a negative amount. Per cent differences from the preceding year are shown in the chart, Fig. 5-13.

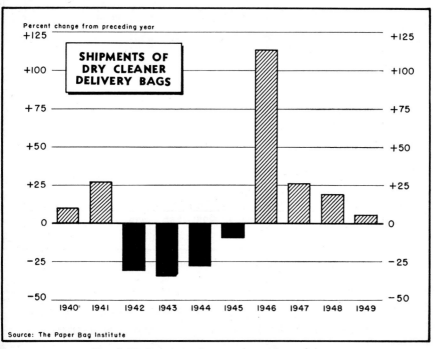

Fig. 5-13. Per cent change shown by columns.

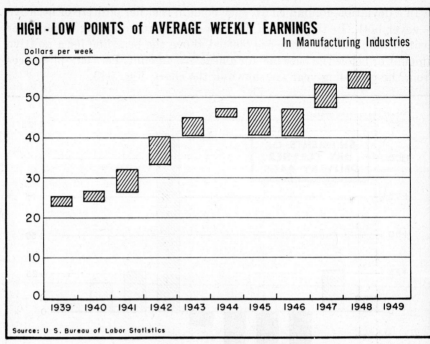

Fig. 5-14. A high-low chart indicating a range.

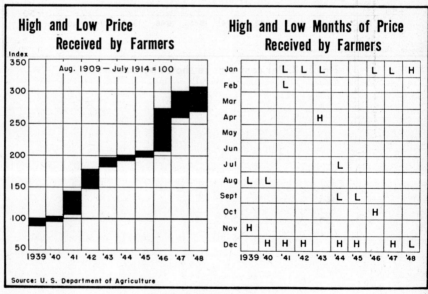

Fig. 5-15. A high-low score.

High-low Charts

The high-low chart allows for the plotting of a maximum and a minimum value for specified periods of time. The top of the column represents the high value and the bottom, the low. The distance between the maximum and the minimum indicates the range of the data for that particular period. The plottings may be averages for weeks, months, etc., or for quotations as of certain specified dates. The chart, Fig. 5-14, gives the high and low average weekly earnings in manufacturing.

This type of chart appears frequently in weather reports of the high and low temperatures of the day and month. It is also seen in the familiar stock-market reports showing the high and low points in the stock transactions of the day.

Averages for the day or, in the case of stocks, the opening or closing point for the day, may be indicated by the use of a heavy horizontal line across the column or some type of symbol indicating a specific amount on the column.

The high-low chart is particularly effective for showing price data. The chart, Fig. 5-15, shows not only the high-low price index, but also the high and low months for prices received by farmers during the year; high and low are indicated on the second part of the chart by H and L.

TABLE 5-4. PRICE RECEIVED BY FARMERS
August, 1909–July, 1914 = 100

	1939	1940	1941	1942	1943	1944	1945	1946	1947	1948
Jan.	96	100	*107*	*148*	*181*	196	201	*206*	*260*	**307**
Feb.	95	103	*107*	150	184	195	199	207	262	279
Mar.	95	103	108	151	192	196	198	209	280	283
Apr.	94	102	115	155	**197**	196	203	212	276	291
May	93	101	116	154	194	194	200	211	272	289
June	91	97	120	154	195	193	206	218	271	295
July	91	97	126	157	193	*192*	206	244	276	301
Aug.	*89*	*96*	130	160	192	193	204	249	276	293
Sept.	98	98	138	163	193	*192*	*197*	243	286	290
Oct.	99	100	136	167	194	194	199	**273**	289	277
Nov.	**100**	103	137	170	194	196	205	263	287	271
Dec.	98	**104**	**143**	**177**	196	**200**	207	264	**301**	*268*

Note: Figures in italics show the low point for the month. Bold-face figures indicate the high point.

Source: U.S. Department of Agriculture.

The Floating Column

A variation of the subdivided-column is the floating-column chart. In this type, two main components make up the total length of the column. One component is plotted above the base line and the other below; but unlike the deviation-column chart, Fig. 5-12, both plottings are positive amounts. In the chart, Fig. 5-16, the total length of the column represents the gross farm income; the amount above the zero line represents net income, and that below the base represents production expense.

TABLE 5-5. FARM INCOME AND EXPENSES (MILLIONS OF DOLLARS)

	Gross farm income*	Production expenses	Realized net income from agriculture*
1939	$10,547	$ 6,088	$ 4,459
1940	11,009	6,484	4,525
1941	13,881	7,469	6,412
1942	18,551	9,465	9,086
1943	23,008	10,882	12,126
1944	24,159	11,640	12,519
1945	25,419	12,629	12,790
1946	29,255	14,238	15,017
1947	34,643	16,849	17,794
1948	35,299	18,556	16,743

* Includes government payments.
Source: U.S. Department of Agriculture.

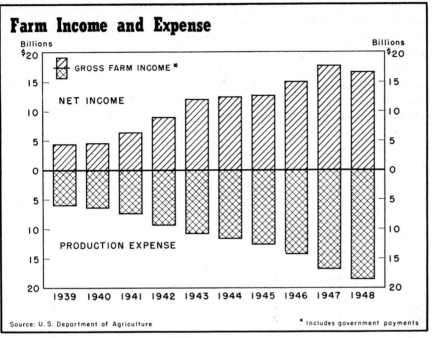

Farm Income and Expense

Billions
$20

GROSS FARM INCOME *

NET INCOME

PRODUCTION EXPENSE

1939 1940 1941 1942 1943 1944 1945 1946 1947 1948

Source: U. S. Department of Agriculture   * Includes government payments

Fig. 5-16. The floating column.

The floating column may also be used effectively in a specialized chart to show the total number of cases on hand and cases handled during a specified time, or for production reports showing relation of contracts completed to contracts incomplete.

The particular layout in the chart, Fig. 5-17, shows the net gain or lag in the work load of a firm at the end of each month. The total length of the column represents the total number of schedules in the office at the end of each time period. The segment above the base line shows the number of schedules completed during the month; the darker segment below the base line indicates those which are incomplete or still on hand. The dotted line on each column marks the amount of monthly lag or gain.

TABLE 5-6. SCHEDULES HANDLED BY COMPANY X IN 1949 (MONTHLY RECORD)

	Total for the month	Number completed	Number incomplete	New schedules during month	Net gain	Net lag
Jan.	440	250	190	240	10	—
Feb.	450	240	210	270	—	30
Mar.	450	270	180	240	30	—
Apr.	420	280	140	240	40	—
May	330	220	110	200	20	—
June	380	210	170	270	—	60
July	320	180	140	160	20	—
Aug.	330	140	190	180	—	40
Sept.	330	190	140	150	40	—
Oct.	410	240	170	260	—	20
Nov.	420	230	190	250	—	20
Dec.	410	290	120	220	70	—

Data assumed.

TURNOVER OF WORKLOAD

As of end of each month   1949

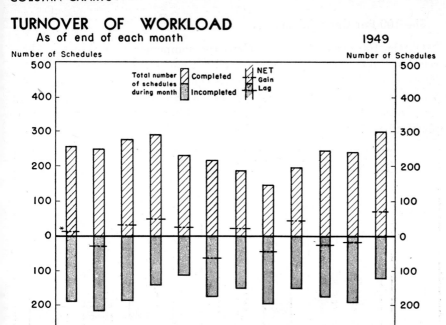

Assumed data

Fig. 5-17. Showing the monthly work load.

The 100 Per Cent Column

On the 100 per cent column chart the components are shown in their relationship to the whole over a period of time. The segment of particular interest should be plotted next to the base line, as it gives the clearer picture and is more easily read (see Fig. 5-18). Keep the segments in the same order throughout the chart. A cumulated table should be made for plotting, as in Tables 4-1, *A* and *B*.

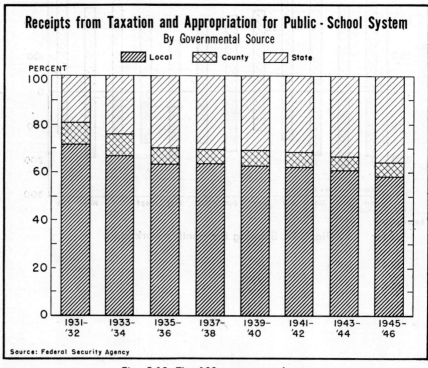

Fig. 5-18. The 100 per cent column.

Illustrations

For more popular presentation, illustrations, pictographs, etc., may be introduced with the columns to add more interest and visual appeal to the plotted story. The chart, Fig. 5-19, gives a graphic and pictorial display of the cost of a typical Thanksgiving dinner on two different dates. This chart is based on average prices for each commodity, weighted by amounts consumed by an average four-person family.

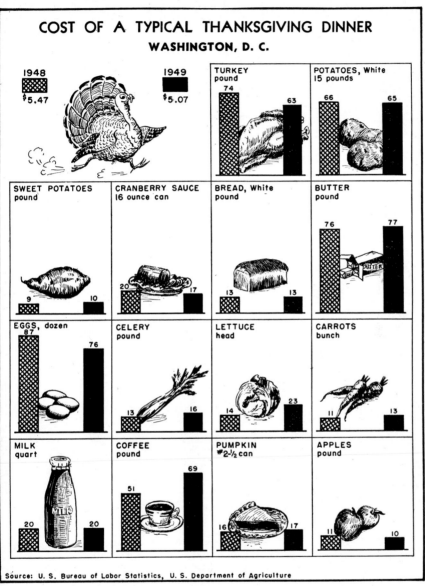

Fig. 5-19. The column chart with pictorial display.

6 • THE BAR CHART

TABLE REVENUE MOTOR BUSES and SCHOOL BUSES					
	School	Local	Intercity	Other	Total
1943	77.9	45.6	28.5	2.0	154.0
1944	75.5	48.5	28.0	3.3	155.3
1945	83.2	46.0	29.0	1.0	159.2
1946	82.5	47.8	30.3	1.5	162.0
1947	85.9	54.1	31.9	3.0	174.9
1948	90.4	57.2	31.8	3.2	182.6 EST.

IN THOUSANDS

Source: Automobile Facts and Figures

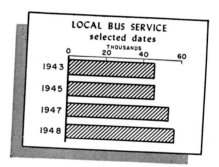

LOCAL BUS SERVICE
selected dates

THE BAR CHART

The horizontal bar chart is the simplest form of graph comparing different items as of a specified date. Like the column chart, it is readily understood. The bars, originating at the right of a common base line, are measured by a few vertical scale lines or ticks.

Spacing of Bars

Ordinarily the spacing between bars is one-half the width of the bar, but the area allotted the chart may cause the width to vary. Do not make the intervening space more than the width of the bar. Too narrow a space would make the bars appear to run together, whereas too wide a space would make them seem lost.

Figure 6-1 compares the per capita consumption of several foods.

TABLE 6-1. CIVILIAN CONSUMPTION OF VEGETABLES, 1949 (POUNDS)

Fresh vegetables	245.0
Canned vegetables	36.4
Potatoes	110.0
Sweet potatoes	14.0
Dry beans (*cleaned*)	8.4

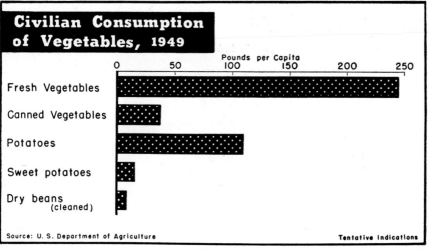

Fig. 6-1. The bar chart.

Labeling Bars

Numerical values may be inserted in the extreme right end of the bar. When this is done, the vertical scale lines are usually omitted. This method gives greater legibility when charts are on display or are to be used in connection with speeches or conferences.

If the bars are not wide enough to allow room for inserting numerals, the data may be lettered to the left of the zero line.

Ample room should be allowed for labeling, whether the lettering is in the stub or directly under the bars. The stub should not dominate the picture, as the bars are the major interest. Various methods for labeling bars may be seen in Fig. 6-2.

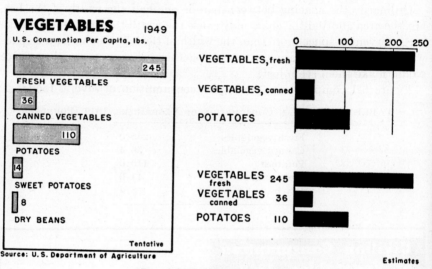

Fig. 6-2. Labeling the bar.

Breaking the Bar

As a rule, bars should not be broken; if they are, a false conclusion can easily be drawn from the graph. If, however, the total length of any one bar is not essential to the whole picture, it may be broken near the end, so long as the numeral is inserted in the broken portion. This numeral should always appear in such cases, whether or not a scale is used. The broken bar in the chart, Fig. 6-3, is allowable, as it can readily be estimated that the elementary schools have three times the enrollment of the secondary schools.

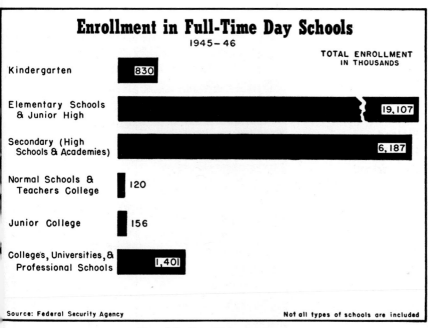

Fig. 6-3. Breaking the bar.

Focal Points

Shading a portion of the background to some division point adds another high light to the chart. In the chart, Fig. 6-4, shading the grid to the 100 base line shows how much above the United States Australia was in the amount of food an hour's work would buy.

A heavy vertical dash line to indicate an average or standard can also add a focal point to the picture (see chart, Fig. 6-5).

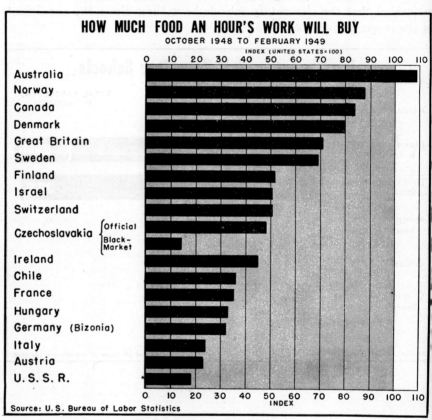

Fig. 6-4. Shading for emphasis.

Arranging the Bars

Bars may be arranged in numerical, alphabetical, progressive, or chronological order. This order depends upon the purpose of the chart and the given data. The name of the category is usually listed to the left of its bar. This list of names forms what is known as the stub.

1. *Numerical order.* When it is intended to show rank or relative position, the multiple-bar chart should be arranged numerically. With the bars plotted in a descending order in the chart, Fig. 6-5, it can be clearly seen which states are above or below the average for the United States.

2. *Alphabetical order.* In an alphabetical arrangement, the amounts will appear irregular, but the categories, or in the case of the chart, Fig. 6-6, the states, may be more readily located. The total of man-days idle is noted in the outline map of the United States.

3. *Progressive order.* The bar chart may be used to advantage for showing progress of some particular project or schedule of work. Processing divisions or objectives are listed to the left of the base line, and the vertical scale carries the units completed or achieved. This method of organization is also used for materiel control charts, Gantt charts (see Fig. 6-28), quota charts, etc. The chart, Fig. 6-7, is a quota chart to be used in a community drive for funds.

4. *Chronological order.* When a few selected dates or periods of time are to be shown, bars may be arranged chronologically. The bar chart should not be used, however, to depict a consecutive trend of a series over a long period of time. The line and column chart are more suited to that type of data (see Figs. 3-3 and 5-1). The chart, Fig. 6-8, shows specified dates which were correctly graphed as a bar chart. Representing the bar as a railroad track adds interest.

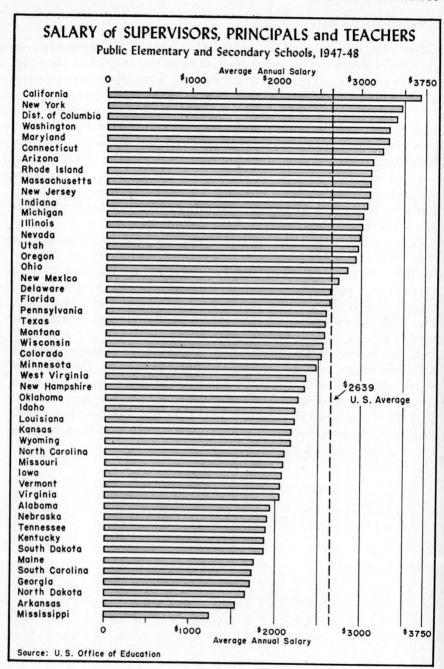

Fig. 6-5. Bars numerically arranged.

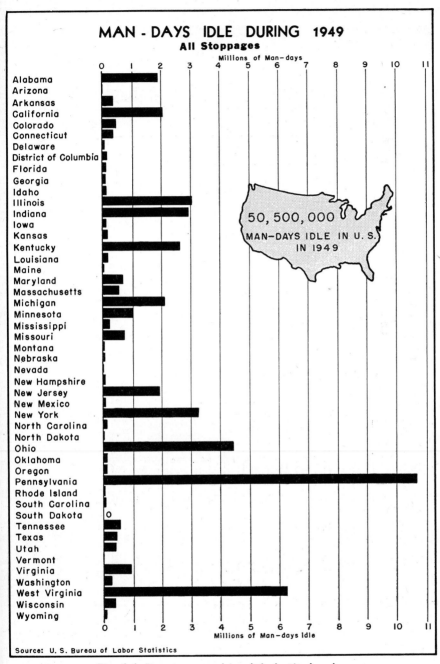

Fig. 6-6. Bars arranged in alphabetical order.

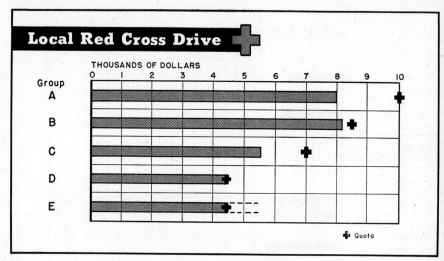

Fig. 6-7. A quota chart.

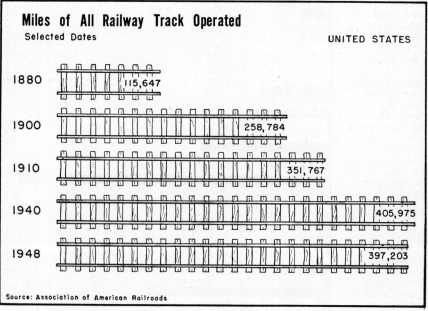

Fig. 6-8. Specified dates represented by pictorial bars.

Qualitative Bars

Qualitative material for one period of time can be particularly well presented in the bar chart. The qualifying attributes are listed to the left of the bar and the horizontal length of the bar designates the amount. The chart, Fig. 6-9, shows the percentage distribution of each cause of death.

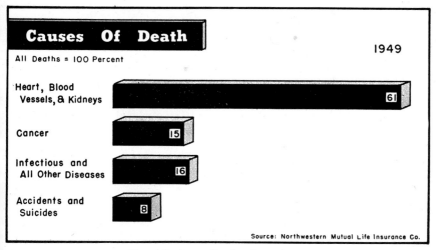

Fig. 6-9. A qualitative bar chart.

Grouped Bars

The grouped-bar chart compares a number of items in two or three respects. The number of bars should be limited to three, as more than that number becomes confusing.

The sequence of the groups, as well as the arrangement within the group, is usually determined by the numerical values of the major category arranged in descending order. Always keep the categories in the same order that was set up in the first group.

A marked contrast in shading should exist between the categories in order that they may be readily distinguished.

Spacing Groups

The space between two-bar groupings ordinarily is the width of one bar. However, if the area allotted is limited, the space between the groups may be slightly narrower, as in the chart, Fig. 6-10. The space between three-bar groupings should be at least one and one-half times the width of one bar.

Legends

A key or legend should be placed in the body of the chart when space permits (see Fig. 6-10). If the bars are of fairly equal length, and space for the legend is limited, the legend may be carried above the horizontal scale (see Fig. 6-14). For a few groups of bars, the chart may appear more balanced if the legend is placed at the bottom of the chart (see Fig. 6-15).

The chart, Fig. 6-10, not only compares white and Negro average salaries but also tells how much those salaries are in certain states. The bars representing the salaries in the white schools, as the larger group, are arranged in numerical sequence.

TABLE 6-2. COMPARATIVE DATA FOR WHITE AND NEGRO SCHOOLS IN 17 STATES AND THE DISTRICT OF COLUMBIA, 1945–1946

Average salary per member of instructional staff

State	White	Negro
Alabama	$1,451	$ 884
Arkansas	1,163	711
Delaware	2,244	1,976
Florida	1,862	1,278
Georgia	1,279	651
Kentucky	1,289	1,367
Louisiana	1,797	948
Maryland	2,297	2,127
Mississippi	1,165	427
Missouri	1,788	1,853
North Carolina	1,608	1,587
Oklahoma	1,807	1,688
South Carolina	1,365	834
Tennessee	1,330	1,044
Texas	1,695	1,315
Virginia	1,605	1,475
West Virginia	1,571	1,789
District of Columbia	2,637	2,637

Source: U.S. Office of Education.

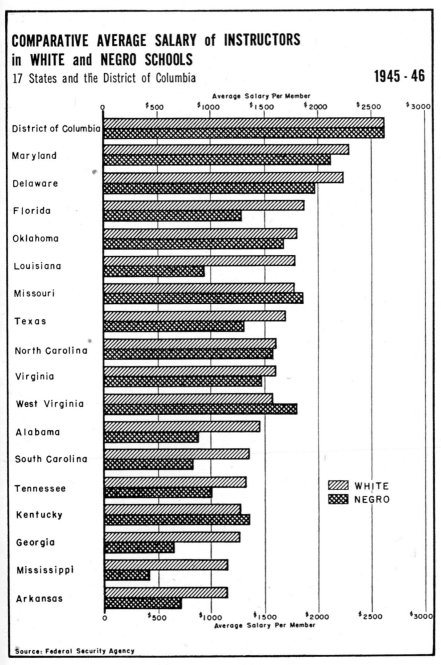

Fig. 6-10. The grouped-bar chart.

Selected Dates

The grouped bar may be used to compare a few selected periods of time. The chart, Fig. 6-11, shows an increase in the number of married women in both population and labor force from 1910 to 1949.

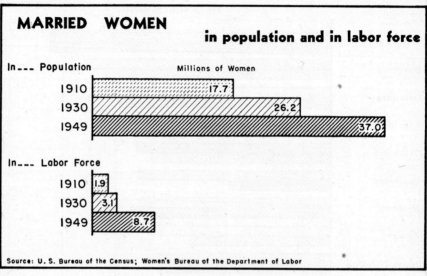

Fig. 6-11. Selected periods compared.

Comparison with a Norm

Comparison with an average, an estimate, a total, or a particular category is quickly obvious in a grouped bar. The chart, Fig. 6-12, shows the striking difference between the costs per pupil in public day school in Mississippi and in Montana and contrasts them with the United States average.

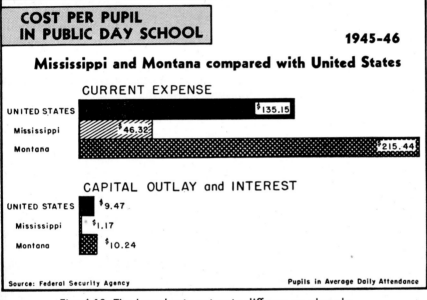

Fig. 6-12. The bar chart contrasts differences sharply.

Subdivided Bars

The subdivided-bar chart gives a general picture of the composition of each bar. The fewer the segments, the easier the chart will be to read. The only true reading of the segments will be the ones adjacent to the base line. Therefore, the more important item should be plotted first. The data in Table 6-3 are plotted as a bar chart in Fig. 6-13 because individual grouping is stressed rather than the very irregular time sequence.

When grouped, the subdivided bars should be limited as to both number of bars in the group and number of segments in each bar. The simpler the chart, the easier it is to read (see chart, Fig. 6-14).

TABLE 6-3. TOTAL FEDERAL RECEIPTS FROM ALCOHOLIC BEVERAGES, SELECTED DATES (MILLIONS OF DOLLARS)

	1933	1939	1941	1945	1948
Distilled spirits	$ 23.4	$353.8	$586.2	$1,701.4	$1,427.0
Beer	114.7	268.6	349.3	661.4	685.2
Wines, cordials, etc.	3.1	13.3	21.8	52.2	67.2
Total	$ 141.2	$635.7	$957.3	$2,415.0	$2,199.8

Source: Bureau of Internal Revenue and Treasury Department.

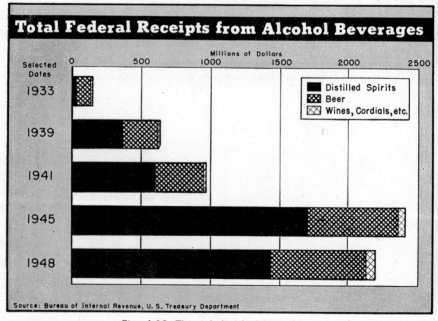

Fig. 6-13. The subdivided-bar chart.

TABLE 6-4. NUMBER OF WOMEN IN EACH AGE GROUP AND NUMBER WHO WERE WORKERS, 1940 AND 1950 (MILLIONS OF WOMEN)

	1940		1950	
Age group	Total number	Number working	Total number	Number working
14–19	7.3	1.4	6.3	1.6
20–34	16.6	6.5	17.9	6.6
35–54	16.5	4.4	19.3	7.2
55 and over	9.8	1.2	12.7	2.4

Source: U.S. Census Bureau.

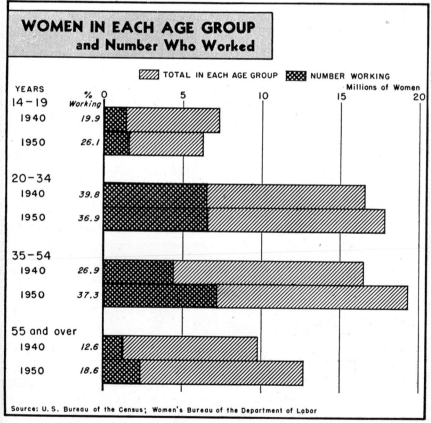

Fig. 6-14. The subdivided grouped-bar chart.

Several groups and subdivisions of bars should be used only for technical analysis and then only by one who is thoroughly familiar with the graph.

100 Per Cent Bars

In the 100 per cent bar chart the bars are of equal length and are divided into segments representing the percentage distribution within each category.

The chart, Fig. 6-15, shows life insurance company mortgage loans by type of property and amount of mortgage. While it is best to keep as few segments as possible in any subdivided bar, in this particular chart the analysis shows a fairly complete breakdown of mortgage loans.

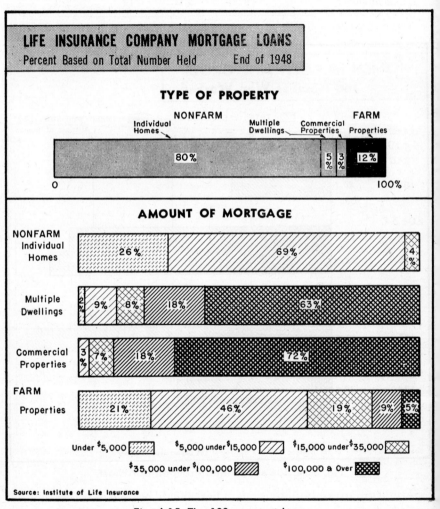

Fig. 6-15. The 100 per cent bar.

In the first part—Type of Property—only two shadings are used to represent nonfarm and farm properties. The nonfarm property breakdown is separated only by heavy lines. Continuous shading is much more pleasing in appearance than a series of different shadings in each segment.

In the lower half of the chart—Amount of Mortgages—the lettering-in of the per cents is a necessity for reading the chart because of the number of segments in each bar and the omission of some of the categories. The per cent sign after the numerals could have been dropped to allow a clearer reading of the amounts. In that case "Per Cent of Loans" would have been used as a subtitle.

The chart, Fig. 6-16, offers a more stylized 100 per cent bar. It makes a simple and effective presentation, provided there are not too many segments.

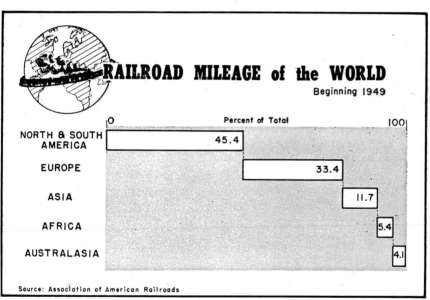

RAILROAD MILEAGE of the WORLD

Beginning 1949

Percent of Total

NORTH & SOUTH AMERICA	45.4
EUROPE	33.4
ASIA	11.7
AFRICA	5.4
AUSTRALASIA	4.1

Source: Association of American Railroads

Fig. 6-16. A step effect presented by separating the segments.

Paired Bars

When it is necessary to compare a number of items in two respects, the paired bar provides a method whereby two different units or scales may be introduced.

The pairs of bars are placed opposite each other, one extending to the right of the listed items and the other to the left. The most important category extends to the right and determines the numerical order of the items. The two scales may relate dollars and pounds, men and payrolls, per cents and actual amounts, tens and hundreds, thousands and millions, etc. Note that both scales are positive amounts. Compare the layout in Fig. 6-17 with the deviation bar (Fig. 6-20), where positive and negative scales are used.

The paired bar is often employed to carry an extended time series. The chart, Fig. 6-18, listing the years 1927–1948, compares workers

TABLE 6-5. EMPLOYMENT AND PAYROLLS IN SELECTED AUTOMOTIVE CONCERNS

Business	Employment March, 1947	Payroll, 1st quarter, 1947 (thousand)
Motor-vehicle and equipment manufacturing	765,708	$541,797
Trucking and warehousing for hire	534,664	314,714
Taxicabs	131,357	55,730
Dealers, new and used motor vehicles	408,802	270,163
Retail filling stations, only	228,952	98,295
Automobile repair and garages	234,209	121,238

Source: Auto Facts, 1949, Automobile Manufacturers' Association, Detroit, Mich.

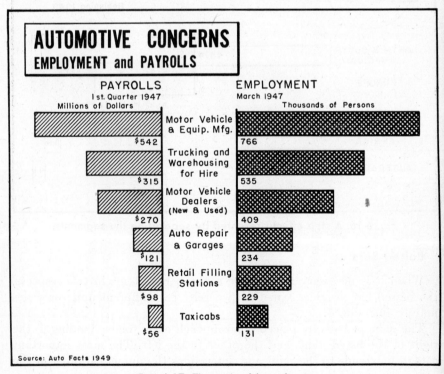

Fig. 6-17. The paired-bar chart.

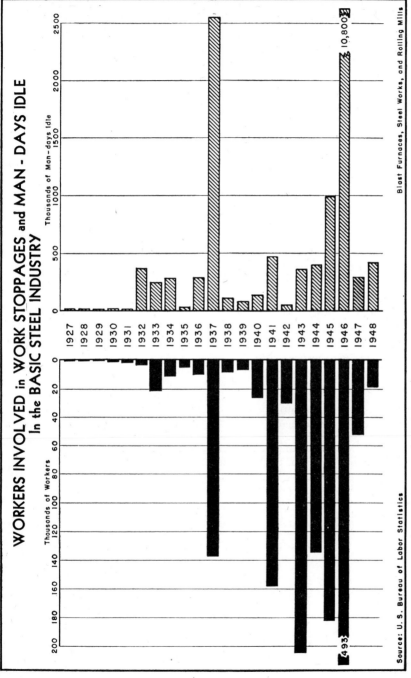

Fig. 6-18. The paired bar used in presenting a time series.

and man-days idle in the basic steel industry by the use of two scales. A multiple-amount-scale curve chart might have been used, since the data cover a period of time. However, the paired bar is the more suitable, because in a multiple-scale line chart (Fig. 3-19) the curves would be too steep to be read accurately.

Bar-and-symbol Charts

The bar-and-symbol chart offers another method of comparing data when a single scale is used. When it is desired to conserve space, this type is usually made instead of the grouped bar. Various symbols or lines may be drawn to spot the point of variance. The chart, Fig. 6-19, makes use of a line symbol to contrast earlier data with a later amount. The 1947 data are represented by a horizontal bar and the 1939 by a heavy vertical line. This chart condenses the presentation and yet tells the story clearly.

TABLE 6-6. WOMEN IN THE FEDERAL SERVICE, WASHINGTON, D.C.

	1939 June 30	1947 June 30
State	477	3,456
Treasury	11,859	13,004
War	2,363	16,125
Justice	1,043	3,327
Post Office	909	1,415
Navy	1,580	10,415
Interior	4,428	1,368
Agriculture	5,545	5,018
Commerce	1,466	4,870
Labor	1,503	1,348

Source: Women's Bureau, U.S. Department of Labor.

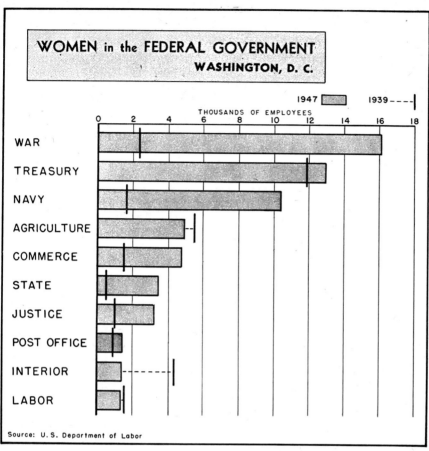

Fig. 6-19. Use of the symbol on a bar chart.

The Deviation Bar

A deviation-bar chart will portray profit and loss, increase and decrease, or similar data. Positive and negative scales extend from either side of a common zero base line. The positive sequence generally extends to the right and is arranged in descending order. The negative sequence, extending to the left of the base line, is arranged in ascending order.

The chart, Fig. 6-20, shows the change in construction costs of one-family homes over a single time interval. Boston costs rose almost as much as San Francisco costs dropped. Charts in Fig. 6-20 and 6-21 show different methods of lettering a deviation chart.

TABLE 6-7. AVERAGE CONSTRUCTION COST OF NEW NONFARM DWELLING
UNITS STARTED

Change in average cost from first two months, 1949,
to first two months, 1950

Area	Dollars
Atlanta	$ 600
Boston	1,100
Chicago	200
Cleveland	700
Denver	−300
Detroit	200
Los Angeles	−800
Miami	−600
New York–northeast New Jersey	−900
Philadelphia	−600
Pittsburgh	−300
San Francisco–Oakland	−1,200
Seattle	600
Washington, D.C.	300

Source: U.S. Department of Labor, Bureau of Labor Statistics.

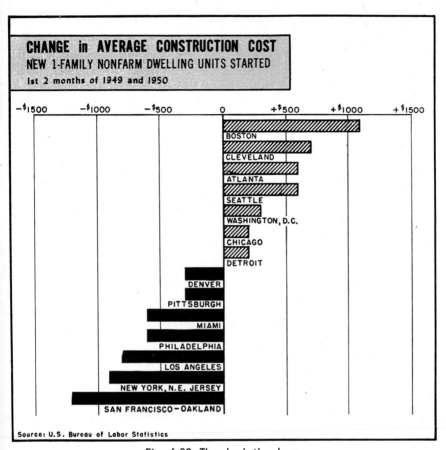

Fig. 6-20. The deviation bar.

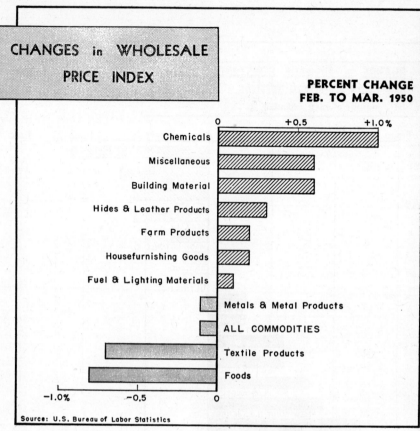

Fig. 6-21. Per cent changes shown by a deviation bar.

The Range Bar

When a comparison of the range—that is, the low and high points—in values, costs, salaries, etc., is to be made for several different items, a range-bar chart will give a simple visual comparison. This type of chart will show the range relationship of each item (see chart, Fig. 6-22).

By the addition of a line symbol to the range chart, supplementary information is given. The chart, Fig. 6-23, not only shows the range of earnings of male clerical workers in Trenton, New Jersey, but gives the weekly salaries in selected occupations. Mode or median can be shown in this manner.

The range-bar chart can also be used to determine a bench mark for judging performance (Fig. 6-24, item *A*). Interquartile range can be indicated clearly on this type of chart (item *B*).

TABLE 6-8. Average Hourly Earnings* in Metalworking Industries in
Trenton, N.J., March, 1949

Occupation	Earnings range of middle 50% of male workers
Assemblers, class B	$1.42–$1.61
Assemblers, class C	1.15– 1.62
Coremakers, hand	1.51– 1.66
Inspectors, class B	1.51– 1.56
Inspectors, class C	1.16– 1.36
Machinists, production	1.30– 1.50
Molders, floor	1.44– 1.60
Punch-press operators, class B	1.41– 1.41
Sheet-metal workers, production	1.10– 1.53
Tool- and die-makers	1.83– 1.97
Welders, hand, class A	1.48– 1.65

* Excludes premium pay for overtime and night work.
Source: U.S. Bureau of Labor Statistics.

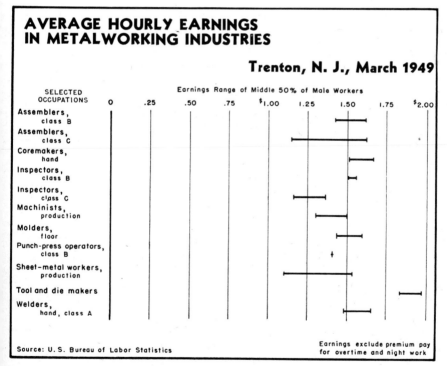

Fig. 6-22. The range bar.

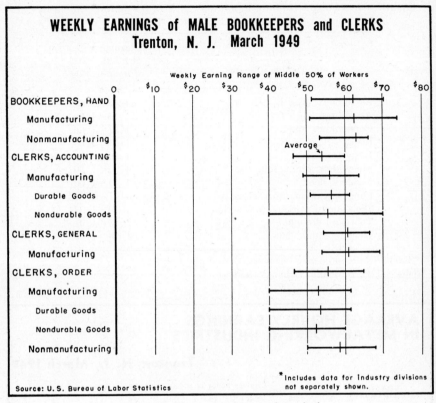

Fig. 6-23. The range bar and symbol.

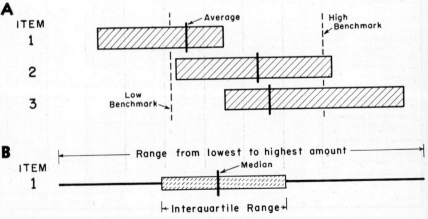

Fig. 6-24. Various uses of the range bar.

Sliding-bar Charts

The sliding-bar chart is one in which the length of a subdivided bar represents a total amount or 100 per cent. It is used when comparing the two main segments of a series of items for a specific time. The main segments are drawn to the left and right of a common base line. These segments in turn may be subdivided, but the divisions should be kept to a minimum.

In the chart, Fig. 6-25, the total length of the bar represents the food dollar. The subdivision of the bar readily shows the farmer's and middleman's share of each item.

Each sliding bar in the chart, Fig. 6-26, represents the total employment in selected office occupations in Trenton, New Jersey. The number of men employed is plotted to the left of the base, or 0 line, and the women to the right. Those working in manufacturing and nonmanufacturing occupations are shown by different styles of crosshatching. The bars are arranged alphabetically by industry group.

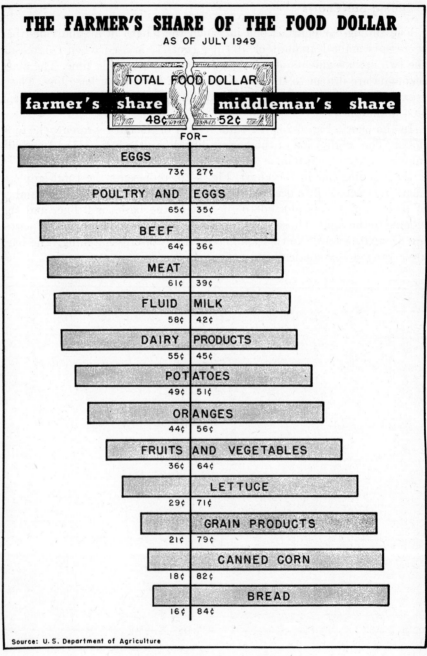

Fig. 6-25. The 100 per cent sliding bar.

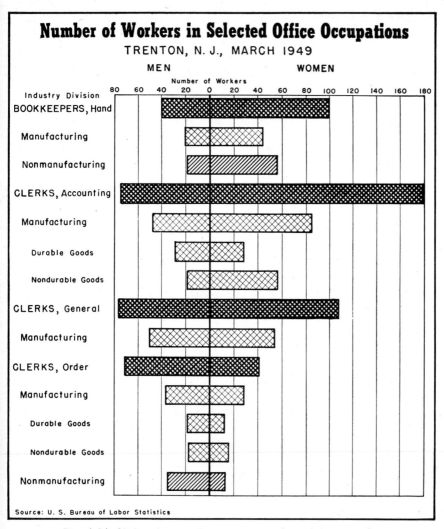

Fig. 6-26. Sliding bar and components plotted separately.

Population Pyramid

The population pyramid is another type of sliding-bar chart commonly used to show the number of men and women comprising each age group. These bars usually are placed in juxtaposition as in the chart, Fig. 6-27. The bar may be subdivided further to show the number of men and women in different occupations. Graphing population and occupations statistics in this fashion is helpful in analyzing the structure of the labor force.

TABLE 6-9. POPULATION OF UNITED STATES, BY SEX AND AGE GROUP, APRIL, 1950
(THOUSANDS OF PERSONS)

	Female	Male	Total
75 years and over	2,100	1,737	3,837
70–74	1,815	1,610	3,425
65–69	2,696	2,364	5,060
60–64	2,921	3,029	5,950
55–59	3,622	3,608	7,230
50–54	4,238	4,036	8,274
45–49	4,470	4,520	8,990
40–44	5,029	5,029	10,058
35–39	5,717	5,476	11,193
30–34	5,866	5,735	11,601
25–29	6,169	5,924	12,093
20–24	5,870	5,457	11,327
15–19	5,431	5,302	10,732
10–14	5,681	5,680	11,361
5– 9	6,416	6,825	13,241
under 5	8,023	8,301	16,324

Source: U.S. Bureau of the Census.

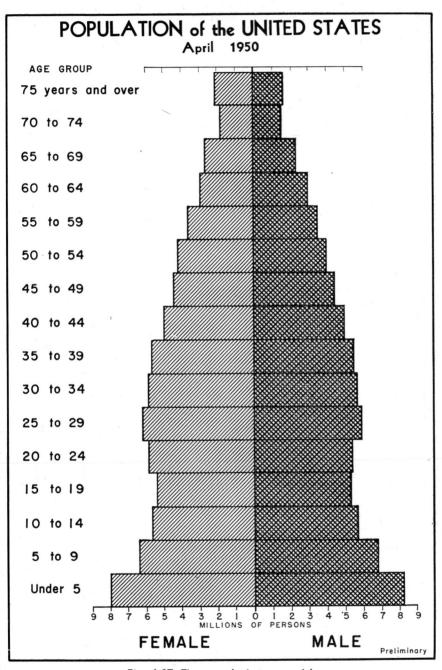

Fig. 6-27. The population pyramid.

TABLE 6-10. Per Cent of Time Machines Were in Operation on Contract Number 699

Each day equals 100 per cent

Section	May 7 Mon.	8 Tues.	9 Wed.	10 Thurs.	11 Fri.	12 Sat.	13 Sun.	Cumulated per cent
1	100	80	100	80	80	80		520
2	W							W
3	60	100	80	20-R				260-R
8	60	40	20-L					120-L

W   Waiting for setup   L   Labor problems
S   Shortage of essential materials   O   Other
R   Repairs

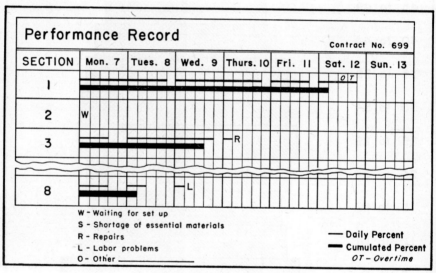

Fig. 6-28. Gantt chart.

The Gantt Chart

The Gantt chart, a progress or control chart, can be used in connection with a wide variety of operations. It may be used to compare a planned schedule of work with the actual performance. It is a convenient tool to use in time and motion study and in individual-performance record analysis.

In an office it can be kept as a daily, weekly, or monthly work chart. A form can be drawn up and kept in a notebook by a supervisor as a record for an individual or group. Or a large wall chart may be hung in the office or production room as an incentive to increase output. Such a chart will help the supervisor to visualize his problems by being able to observe quickly the day-by-day achievement as well as new tendencies in his department.

The Gantt chart is simple to construct. All vertical rulings are uniform, while the horizontal lines mark the time. The first column denotes the department, machine, or materials, etc.; the horizontal rulings are divided into equal spaces representing a period of time. Each of these spaces is subdivided into four or five equal parts representing the per cent of the performance for that set time.

In the chart, Fig. 6-28, the width of the space represents a daily 100 per cent performance record. The light line is the per cent of time the machines were running each day. The heavy bar equals the cumulation of the sum of the light lines, giving a total per cent for the week.

A few possible causes of stoppages are listed as notes, and initials are carried on the body of the chart. This form can serve as a basis for many more elaborate setups.

7 · THE MAP CHART

NUMBER OF CHILDREN CARRIED DAILY IN SCHOOL BUSES By Region 1947-48	
New England	226,000
Mid-Atlantic	649,000
North Central	1,459,000
South Atlantic	1,375,000
South Central	1,381,000
Mountain	202,000
Pacific	429,000

School Buses Carry Over 5 Million Children Daily

IN THOUSANDS

429 202 1459 226 649 1375 1381

Regional 1947-48

The statistical map chart constitutes a striking graphic description of geographic relationship. It should be used, however, only when geographic distribution is of paramount importance and when data can be readily and correctly interpreted in this form.

In making a map chart, exactness is often sacrificed to popular appeal. If precise accuracy in presenting quantitative material is to be maintained, a multiple-bar chart (Figs. 6-5, 6-6) should be planned instead.

The Shaded Map

The shaded or crosshatched map is probably the most frequently used and at the same time most misused. The reason is that the shading of the geographic divisions emphasizes the extent of surface area at the expense of the statistical unit. Data to be presented in a surface map should definitely be in terms of area. The misreading of nonarea data on the shaded map is mainly due to the fact that, even though a large area and a small area bear the same shading, they do not visually assume the same magnitude.

The shading patterns should run progressively from dark to light, depending upon the emphasis desired in the data. Arranging the data in numerical order will help decide which gradation of shading to allocate to which frequency unit. Tables 7-1A and B show a sample work sheet for grouping the data. Try to keep the distribution intervals equal—for instance, under 50, 50 and under 100, 100 and under 150, 150 and over.

Methods of Shading

The commercially printed crosshatchings and shadings of today and the chemically prepared papers and film overlays, make it possible to save time by cutting out areas and applying them to a map. They have the added advantage that the patterns and densities are uniform. The shading patterns should be distinctive in order that differences in area may be readily contrasted and that similar situations may be easily compared. Use as few patterns as possible—not over four or five.

TABLE 7-1A. PERCENTAGE OF THE POPULATION AGED 65 AND OVER IN EACH STATE

State	%	State	%
Total U.S.	7.5	Montana	9.0
Alabama	5.3	Nebraska	9.4
Arizona	5.5	Nevada	7.0
Arkansas	6.1	New Hampshire	9.9
California	7.9	New Jersey	7.4
Colorado	8.6	New Mexico	4.6
Connecticut	8.0	New York	8.2
Delaware	8.2	North Carolina	5.1
D. of C.	5.9	North Dakota	8.2
Florida	7.6	Ohio	8.3
Georgia	5.4	Oklahoma	7.1
Idaho	6.9	Oregon	7.0
Illinois	8.1	Pennsylvania	7.6
Indiana	8.3	Rhode Island	8.7
Iowa	9.9	South Carolina	4.4
Kansas	9.1	South Dakota	8.3
Kentucky	7.5	Tennessee	6.5
Louisiana	5.5	Texas	5.9
Maine	9.3	Utah	5.9
Maryland	6.8	Vermont	10.0
Massachusetts	9.1	Virginia	6.1
Michigan	6.8	Washington	7.4
Minnesota	8.5	West Virginia	6.3
Mississippi	5.8	Wisconsin	8.8
Missouri	9.8	Wyoming	6.0

TABLE 7-1B. TABLE ARRANGED NUMERICALLY TO DETERMINE INTERVAL GROUPINGS FOR SHADING ON MAP

State	%	State	%
Under 6		Kentucky	7.5
South Carolina	4.4	Pennsylvania	7.6
New Mexico	4.6	Florida	7.6
North Carolina	5.1	California	7.9
Alabama	5.3	**8 and under 9**	
Georgia	5.4	Connecticut	8.0
Louisiana	5.5	Illinois	8.1
Arizona	5.5	Delaware	8.2
Mississippi	5.8	New York	8.2
Texas	5.9	North Dakota	8.2
Utah	5.9	Ohio	8.3
D. of C.	5.9	South Dakota	8.3
6 and under 7		Indiana	8.3
Wyoming	6.0	Minnesota	8.5
Arkansas	6.1	Colorado	8.6
Virginia	6.1	Rhode Island	8.7
West Virginia	6.3	Wisconsin	8.8
Tennessee	6.5	**9 and under 10**	
Michigan	6.8	Montana	9.0
Maryland	6.8	Massachusetts	9.1
Idaho	6.9	Kansas	9.1
7 and under 8		Maine	9.3
Nevada	7.0	Nebraska	9.4
Oregon	7.0	Missouri	9.8
Oklahoma	7.1	New Hampshire	9.9
Washington	7.4	Iowa	9.9
New Jersey	7.4	Vermont	10.0

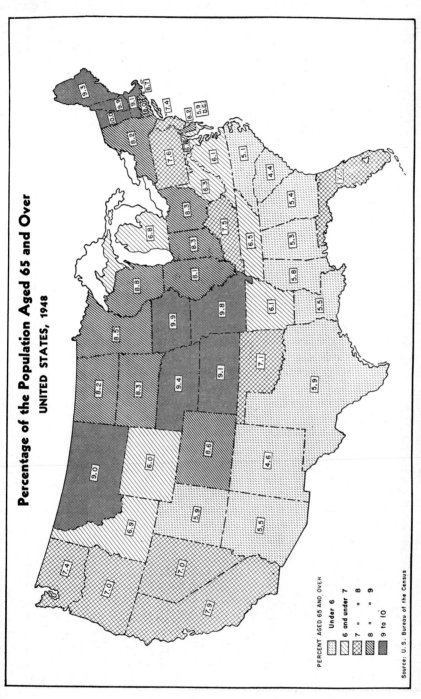

Percentage of the Population Aged 65 and Over
UNITED STATES, 1948

PERCENT AGED 65 AND OVER
Under 6
6 and under 7
7 " " 8
8 " " 9
9 to 10

Source: U. S. Bureau of the Census

Fig. 7-1. The shaded quantitative map.

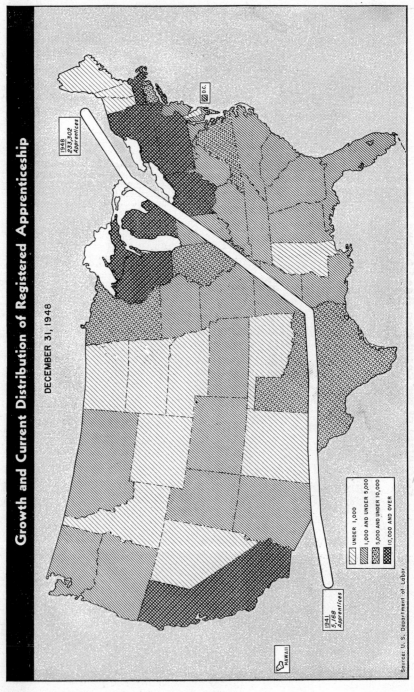

Fig. 7-2. The map with trend superimposed.

Quantitative Maps

The quantitative map shows frequency distribution relative to an area. The shading and crosshatching identify by ascending order of intensities, in which numerical or percentage group each state or area falls. The map in Fig. 7-1 shows the percentage of persons sixty-five years of age and over in each state.

The map in Fig. 7-2 shows the distribution of registered apprentices by four frequency shadings. In addition, a seven-year trend was superimposed, showing the growth in the number of apprentices between 1941 and 1948.

White Areas

All areas that have some numerical or qualitative value should bear a shading. An area is left white only when that particular portion of the map is not under discussion, as in the map in Fig. 7-3. However, in a stylized map, a white area may assume a numerical value if black and grays are used as background.

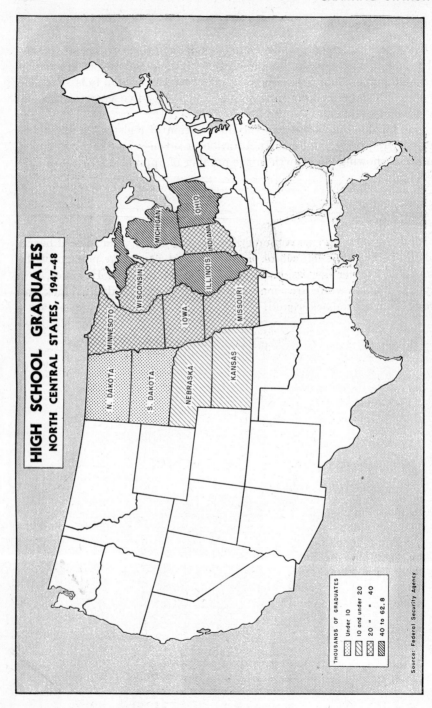

Fig. 7-3. White areas denoting no data.

Qualitative Maps

Those maps on which data are qualifying, such as states for or against a wage law, or those showing political preference, or a world map showing religious, military, or economic situations are known as qualitative maps.

They are particularly adapted to shading and crosshatching. As a rule not many shadings are required to designate characteristics of an area (see map, Fig. 7-4).

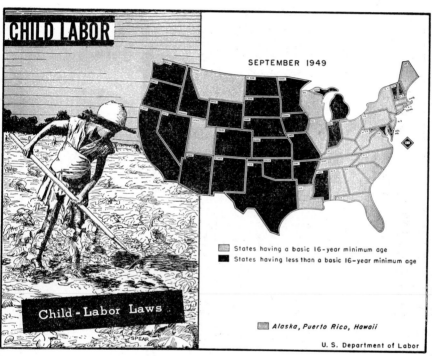

Fig. 7-4. The qualitative map.

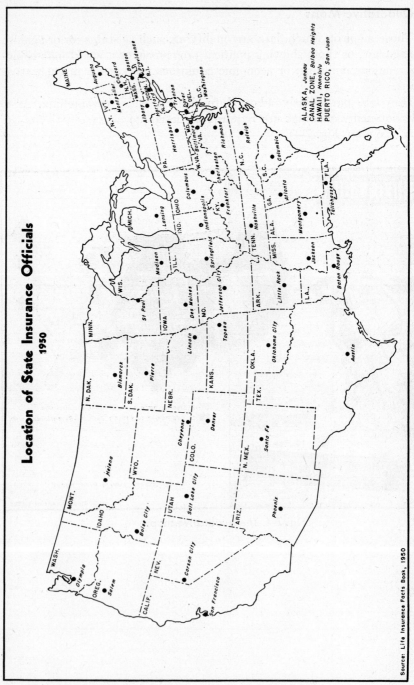

Fig. 7-5. The dot-location map.

Dot Location

There are many varieties of dot-map charts and they are used in many ways. The dot-location map shows the dot in the exact geographic location of the data described (see map, Fig. 7-5). This type is often used in the form of a pin or tack map, showing where representatives of a company are located, where branch stores are situated, where surveys are to be made, and for similar data.

Dot Density

Geographic distribution is presented effectively by a dot-density map. In this, the dots representing numerical values are plotted in the approximate geographic location. Here dots closely concentrate around a particular locale (see map, Fig. 7-6).

Dot-density plotting shows up best when the data are concentrated in small areas, as for showing crop production in counties, or the number of accidents at street intersections of a city.

Dots Showing Numerical Value

Dots representing a numerical value may be arranged systematically within the geographic area. In the map in Fig. 7-7, the reader can get a graphic comparison of quantities. If he wants a more precise reading, he can count the number of dots. In the case of the small northeastern states where so often the data is a large amount, the dots extend over the coast line rather than overlap one another.

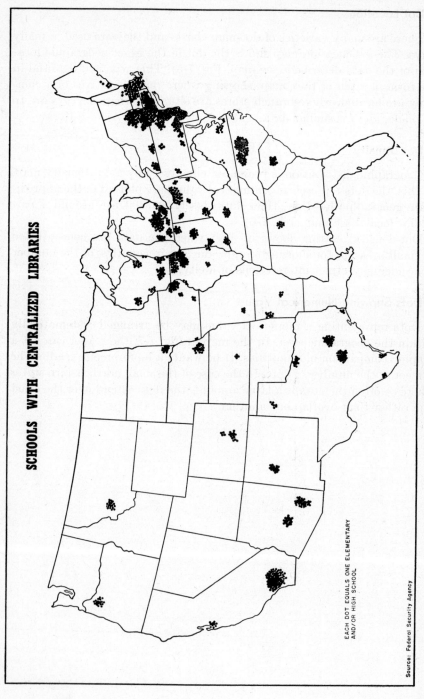

Fig. 7-6. The dot-concentration map.

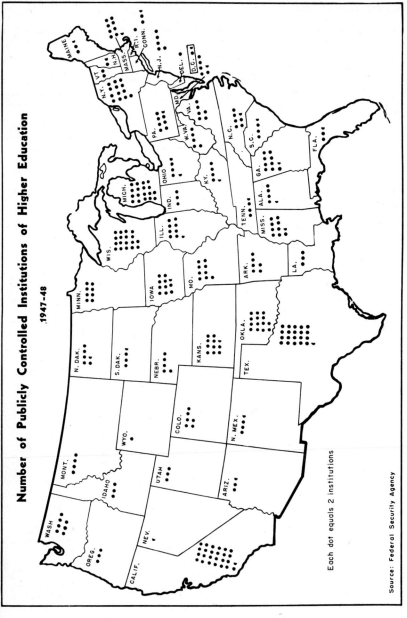

Number of Publicly Controlled Institutions of Higher Education
1947-48

Each dot equals 2 institutions

Source: Federal Security Agency

Fig. 7-7. Dot with numerical values.

Varying Size of Dot

Variations in quantities may also be shown by using dots or circles of unlike size and shading. When many dots or circles are used on a map of this type, a diametric scale should be drawn in conjunction with the legend (see map, Fig. 7-8). This will facilitate reading the sizes of the circles when they are not adjacent. If dots are few, actual figures may appear beneath the circle.

Sector Dot

Circles on the map may show not only the geographic location of the data and the amount (size of the circle), but also a further breakdown within the circle, either quantitative (showing per cents) or qualitative (showing types). However, when the map contains too much information, it loses its value as a visual tool.

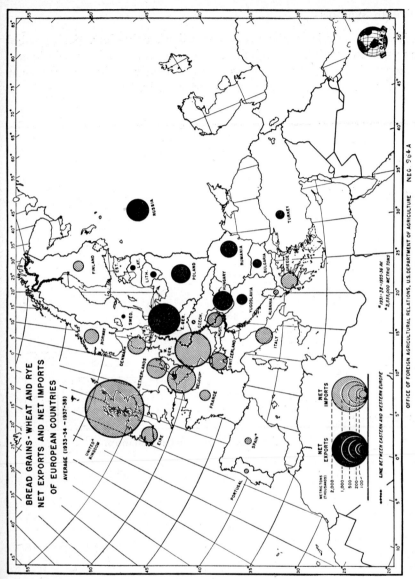

Fig. 7-8. Dot of varying size.

Diverse Symbols

Diverse geometric symbols may be used with the dots. Each symbol represents one variable. Graduated size of each symbol may designate another variable, either qualitative or quantitative. The symbols must be clearly defined in concise legend (see map, Fig. 7-9).

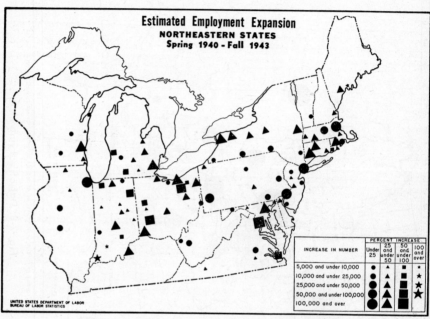

Fig. 7-9. Use of geometric symbols on map.

Pictorial Symbols on Maps

Pictorial symbols instead of geometric symbols add interest to a map, particularly when the map is to be used in a display, an exhibit, or in a company report. Each symbol is given a numerical value. The symbol should be designed to refer to the subject, and should still be a legible object when only half of it is drawn (see example in Chapter 8, Fig. 8-12).

In Fig. 7-10 a pictorial symbol is used in plotting the data. The line below the symbols gives a correct numerical plotting, while each symbol represents a partial or full unit of measure. In this case each symbol equals ten men (see page 208 and Fig. 8-13 for dividing the symbol).

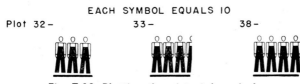

EACH SYMBOL EQUALS 10

Plot 32 –   33 –   38 –

Fig. 7-10. Plotting the pictorial symbol.

Pictorial Maps

Illustrations or pictographs used in a qualitative pictorial map carry a fairly complete story of the subject (see map, Fig. 7-11). Here the pictograph represents the chief materials that could be contributed by each area.

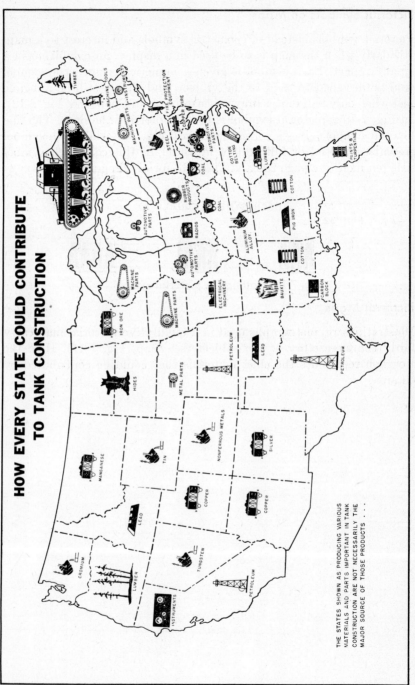

Fig. 7-11. Map illustrated with pictographs.

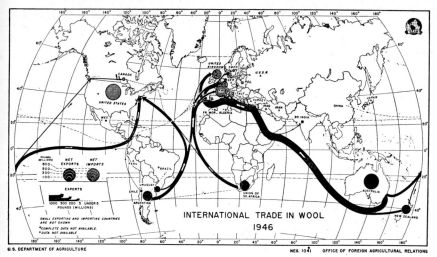

Fig. 7-12. The flow map.

Flow Maps

The flow map delineates route by directional flow lines; it suggests capacity or volume by width of line. The map in Fig. 7-12 dramatizes the international trade in wool by tracing the path of travel from production area to destination.

8 • OTHER TYPES AND THEIR USE

TABLE	REVENUE MOTOR BUSES and SCHOOL BUSES				
	School	Local	Intercity	Other	Total
1943	77.9	45.6	28.5	2.0	154.0
1944	75.5	48.5	28.0	3.3	155.3
1945	83.2	46.0	29.0	1.0	159.2
1946	82.5	47.8	30.3	1.5	162.0
1947	85.9	54.1	31.9	3.0	174.9
1948	90.4	57.2	31.8	3.2	182.6

IN THOUSANDS   EST.

Source: Automobile Facts and Figures

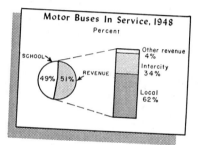

The Pie Chart

The pie or sector chart makes a comparison of various components with each other and with the whole. However, this type should be used sparingly, especially when there are many segments. It is not only difficult to compare area segments, but most difficult to label them properly. When there are many divisions of the data, a bar chart would give greater clarity (see Fig. 8-1).

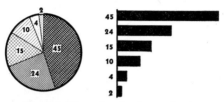

Fig. 8-1. Use pie chart sparingly.

In the chart, Fig. 8-2, the percentage participation of women in several different categories is graphically portrayed. Each sector tells its own story; that is, of the total population of fourteen years and over, 51 per cent were women; of the total civilian labor force, 29 per cent were women; and so on.

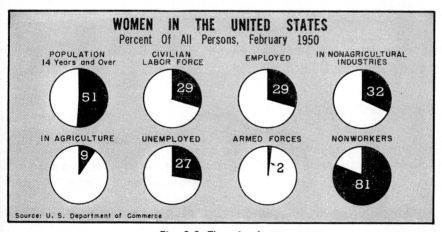

Fig. 8-2. The pie chart.

197

The pie chart, with one or two sectors representing percentages or parts of a dollar, can be used very effectively as a graphic advertisement or for offering information to the public. It appears chiefly in annual reports. However, in budgets or tax breakdowns, or data where there are many sectors involved, it is likely to become too complicated to label clearly. Fig. 8-3 shows a good example of the pie chart for display purposes.

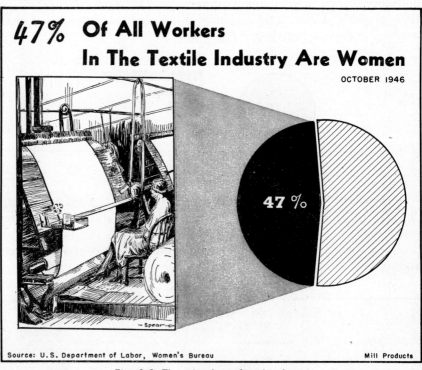

Fig. 8-3. The pie chart for displays.

Pie and Column

The chart, Fig. 8-4, depicts an unusual combination of the pie and the column. The shaded sector of the pie represents those engineers who were educated in one particular field of engineering and were employed in that same field. The white sector measures the remainder, who were employed in another field. This white sector was extended to form a percentage column with subdivisions showing the fields to which these engineers transferred.

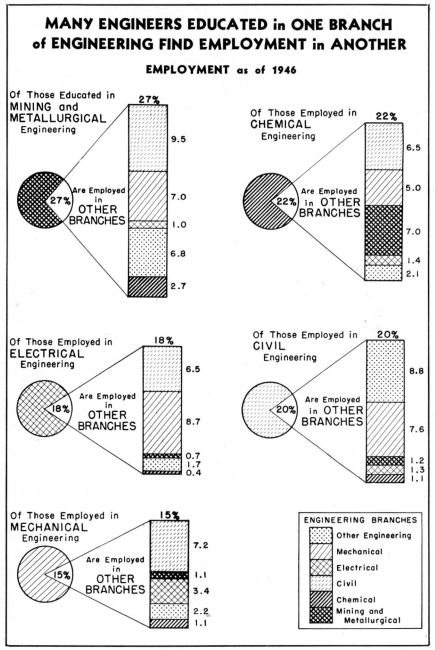

Fig. 8-4. Combining the pie and column.

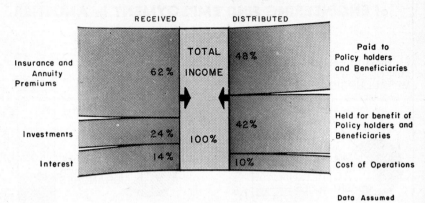

Fig. 8-5. The cosmograph.

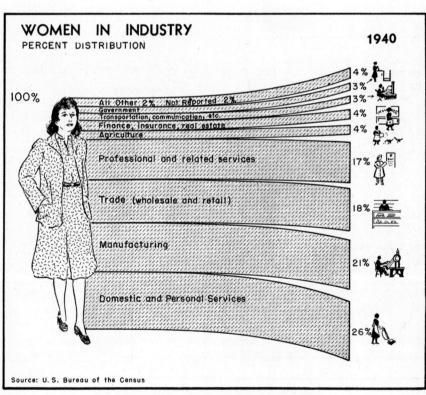

Fig. 8-6. The 100 per cent flow chart.

The Cosmograph

The term cosmograph applies both to the manufactured mechanical device and to the graphic chart which shows counterbalancing items and their distribution. A cosmograph is especially useful in the presentation of a balance sheet, status report, payroll and payroll distribution, income and expenditures.

As a mechanical device, it consists of a black-background board on which 1,000 strips of white paper are securely fastened. This forms a 100 per cent column. The ends of the paper are separated into groups representing the desired percentages and clamped firmly in position. Red and blue markers facilitate the counting of the strips.

The cosmograph in its chart form may be represented by a column, a stack of dollars, or other pictorial symbol, with segments spreading fan-like to the left and right. As a rule the left designates the income item and the right the outgo distribution.

The chart, Fig. 8-5 is used to show income received (left) and money distributed (right).

The cosmograph can be used to advantage in presenting a single distribution in which there are many segments making up a total (Fig. 8-6).

Process-flow Chart

The work-flow or process chart is equally useful in showing how a shirt is made, how a rubber tire is manufactured, or the steps taken to change a bushel of grain into a loaf of bread. In Fig. 8-7, the flow of work in three printing processes, letterpress, lithographic, and rotogravure, is followed through from the original copy to the customer.

Action-flow Chart

Figure 8-8 is one of four flow layouts depicting what happens to a bill from the time it is presented to Congress until it becomes a law or is defeated. In this layout, the Senate action is clearly defined, step by step, by following the numbered directional lines. The bill is received from the House and, if the action at each step is favorable, it may finally be passed to the President for further consideration.

This type of chart is used to excellent advantage in explaining a flow of action if there are many alternatives and a description in words is tedious and hard to follow without the illustration.

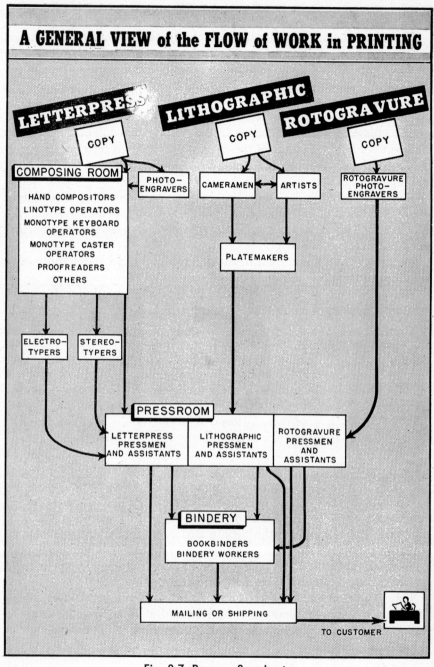

Fig. 8-7. Process-flowchart.

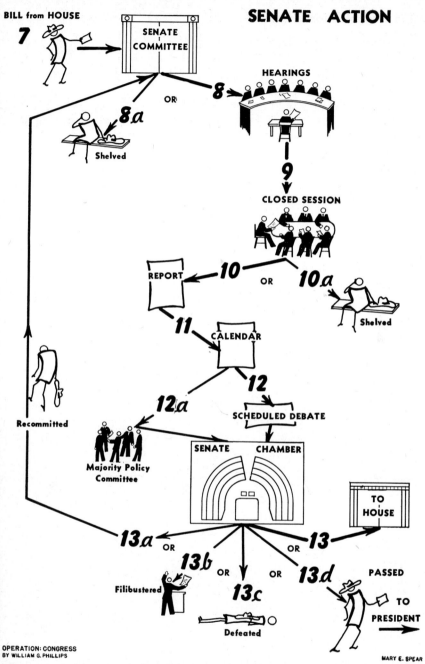

Fig. 8-8. Action-flow chart.

The Organization Chart

The organization chart follows the pattern of the flow chart. It may show the rank of the officials in an organization or the functions of each department. Again, it may show the title and salary of each employee as part of a budget presentation.

Every organization and business should have some plan of organization layout in plain view. It shows the employee how he ranks in the organization, who his immediate superior is, and who is in charge of other departments with which he may come into contact. Such a chart helps in visualizing the whole personnel structure of the business.

In the organization chart the flow line should diminish in weight as the order of responsibility branches down. The flow line should be of definitely greater weight than the outline of the boxes. Thus the eye can follow the progression without interruption.

Figure 8-9 shows the Overseas Information Program of the ECA. This is an example of a well-organized visual-information program using publishing, radio, broadcasting, exhibits, and films as media for publicity.

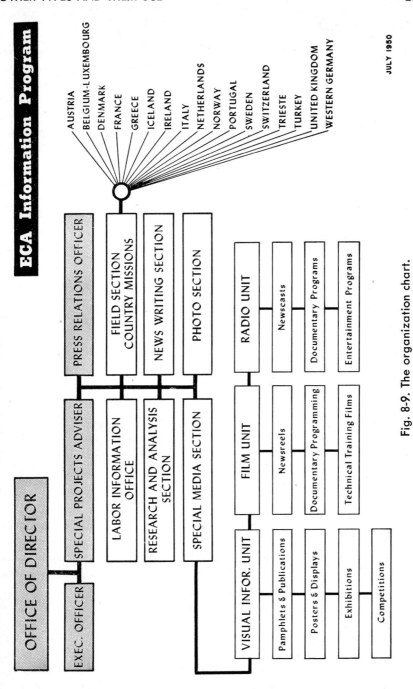

Fig. 8-9. The organization chart.

The Pictograph

The pictograph illustrates statistical data by means of a pictorial symbol. It can add greatly to the interest of what might otherwise be a dull subject. The chosen symbol must have a close association with the subject matter, so that the reader can comprehend the subject under discussion at a glance. The pictograph is admirably adapted to the illustration of exhibits or articles in newspapers and magazines, or for dressing up annual reports. The chart, Fig. 8-10, follows through with a message by using representative pictographs.

Fig. 8-10. The pictograph.

Pictorial Symbols

A pictograph should be designed for each individual category. However, if this is not always possible, most commonly used symbols may be obtained from firms engaged in this type of designing for graphic presentation. The pictorial symbols in Fig. 8-11 were especially designed as part of an occupation series.

PICTORIAL SYMBOLS

Soldier	Judge	Grocer
Sailor	Policeman	Farmer
Aviator	Fireman	Miner
Teacher	Unemployed	Carpenter

Fig. 8-11. Pictorial symbol.

Dividing the Symbol

In Fig. 8-12, *A* and *B* can be identified as a house or a man from the portion drawn, but in *C* half a horse, representing horsepower, keeps the reader guessing. Pictorial devices that cannot be divided and still leave the identity clear should be avoided.

Fig. 8-12. Dividing the symbol.

Volume Symbols

The volume diagram comparison is frequently incorrectly drawn because the third dimension is ignored. The correct method can best be illustrated by means of a problem.

Suppose we wish to represent the food dollar as being able to buy 20 pounds of potatoes in 1939 and only 10 pounds in 1950. We wish to use a basket as our symbol. The difference in dimensions should be computed on the volume basis as follows:

Step 1. Divide the 1939 amount by that for 1950 and extract the cube root of the result: $\frac{20}{10} = 2$. The cube root of $2 = 1.26$.

Step 2. Multiply the 1950 pictorial symbol dimensions by the cube root of the quotient (in this case 1.26) to obtain the 1939 dimensions.

Thus, if the 1950 basket was 1.2 by 0.4 by 1 inch and we multiply these dimensions by 1.26, we find that the 1939 basket would be 1.512 by .504 by 1.26 inches.

This enlargement should be used, even though the thickness of a symbol is not shown and only two dimensions are indicated.

The Pictogram

The pictogram is a pictorial-unit bar chart in which each symbol is given a numerical value. The rows of symbols are styled in such a way that each bar is immediately identified with its stub.

In laying out the row of symbols, arrange them on a line plotted to the correct numerical length (see chart, Fig. 8-13). In representing fractions of units, the symbol should be dropped if the fraction is less than one quarter. One quarter to three quarters of the unit should be represented by half a figure; more than three quarters should be drawn as a whole symbol. The plotted line will show the actual amount of data, though the figures or symbols may show a little more or a little less.

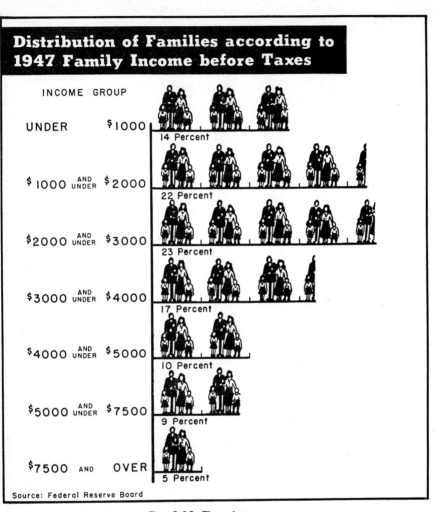

Fig. 8-13. The pictogram.

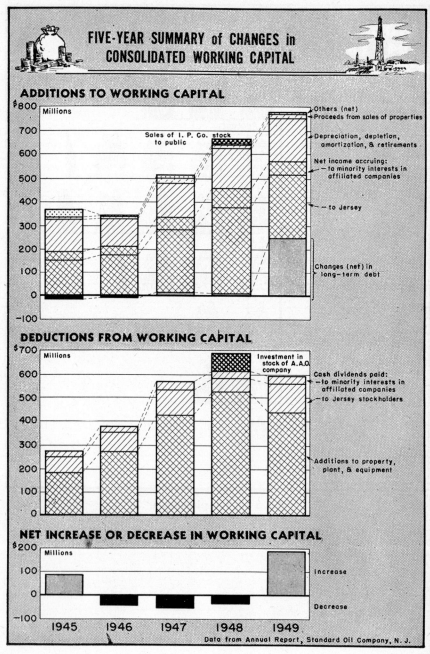

Fig. 8-14. A company report.

Reports

In recent years, company and organization reports have become works of art. Every skill of the printing craft and technique of the drafting room has been applied in their embellishment. Some of these are excellent presentations, but others confuse and distort the facts. Probably a great deal of good will has been built up by those companies that have tried to make their financial statements intelligible to the average person, who so often finds great masses of figures very confusing. The three examples of reports reproduced in this section are of a statistical nature with a great deal of detail. They are easier to understand and analyze than if they were written out in text or itemized in tables.

The chart, Fig. 8-14, gives the breakdown first of additions to the working capital, then of deductions. In summary, the last part shows at a glance the net increase or decrease.

The members of the congregation of the Presbyterian Church in Katoma Park will be able to vote more wisely on where and how to distribute the funds at their disposal when they have the chart in Fig. 8-15 to use as a guide.

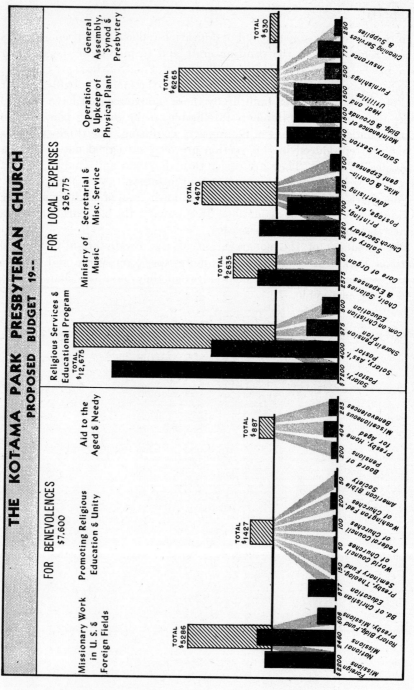

Fig. 8-15. A budget.

Statements

The chart, Fig. 8-16, presents an annual financial statement in the form of a pictorial column. These data could also be worked into a flow chart or cosmograph (see Fig. 8-5), with the funds applied fanning to the left and the funds provided fanning to the right. This is the type of layout an accountant might use to advantage.

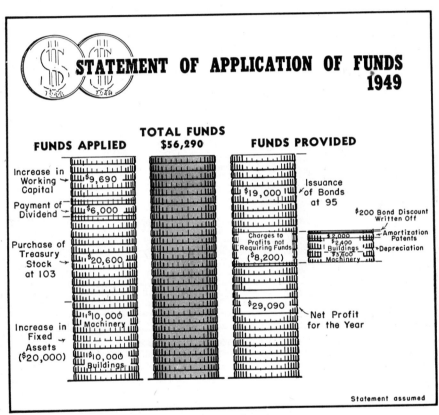

Fig. 8-16. Financial statement.

Illustrations

Illustrations and shading add to the interest of an otherwise common-place chart. The chart, Fig. 8-17, shows the shift of farm population. Only in 1945 and 1946 were gains registered. These gains are explained by the return of large numbers of soldiers from the front, after hostilities ended.

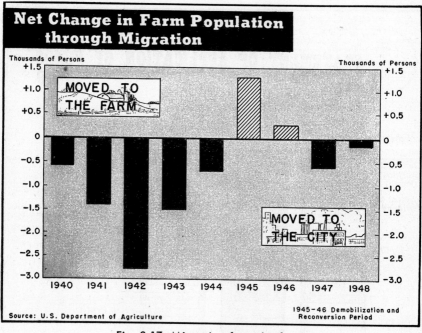

Fig. 8-17. Migration from the farm.

Cartoons

Cartoons abound in newspapers and magazines. Charts are frequently used as the peg on which to hang this form of humor. A possible cartoon could be drawn with two burglars kneeling beside a gaping safe, which they have obviously jimmied. The safe is completely empty. They are studying a chart, which shows the asset curve of the company dropping down and even off the chart. The caption might read, "We should have looked here first."

The Jim Berryman cartoon (Fig. 8-18) is reproduced here by the courtesy of the *Evening Star* of Washington, D.C. It was printed on March 26, 1949, at a time when prices had registered a slight percentage drop for the month, although they had been steadily rising over a period of two or three years. As with most cartoons, it is necessary to know what event inspired the drawing.

Fig. 8-18. The cartoon.

9 • EXHIBITS

Fig. 9-1. Panel exhibit.

EXHIBITS

Exhibits play an important part in telling a story to the public. Very few persons can resist stopping before an attractive display. Exhibits are often used by business firms in explaining production and research activities to the public, as training devices for new employees, to analyze the health of the firm's financial condition, and to ascertain which procedures are valuable and which produce only deadwood.

Progressive schools use many visual aids to save the pupil's time in learning as well as the instructor's time in teaching. Not only are these techniques timesavers, but they also offer the information in a vivid way that enables the student to remember the facts better.

The exhibit should be planned simply and with a direct message. Too many flourishes kill the story.

Posters

The poster is the simplest type of exhibit. A good poster should make one and only one direct statement. This can be done with a few pertinent words and by utilizing a chart, diagram, picture, or anything that will help to present the facts or emphasize the idea.

The poster must be simple in design, with its message so compactly stated that it can be understood at a glance.

Panel Exhibits

The panel exhibit is more or less an elaboration of the poster, in that it may present several related ideas. In Fig. 9-1, the center panel "Jobs for Veterans" could be used as a poster. The other two panels bring in a further idea of employing the handicapped.

Table-top Displays

Figure 9-2 not only pictures an industrial safety program, but also exhibits pamphlets relative to carrying out safety measures.

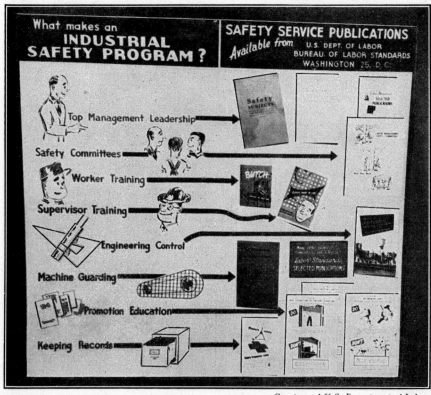

Courtesy of U.S. Department of Labor.

Fig. 9-2. Pamphlet display.

In Fig. 9-3, the panels could be used separately, but for exhibit purposes, they form a well-planned unit. This folding panel is a table-top display about 3 feet high.

The three-panel exhibit in Fig. 9-4 is a continuous unit. It is eye-catching and informative. Supplementary material could be placed on the table, but arranged so that it does not obstruct the view of the exhibit.

Fig. 9-3. Table-top display.

Fig. 9-4. Unit panels.

Panel Screen

Figure 9-5 is a three-panel screen about 5 feet high. Two-way hinges were used so that another story idea could be elaborated on the back. The opposite sides could carry supplementary material, and the screen could be displayed in the center of the exhibit area, with all six surfaces visible. Or the two sides of the screen could be unrelated and used on different occasions.

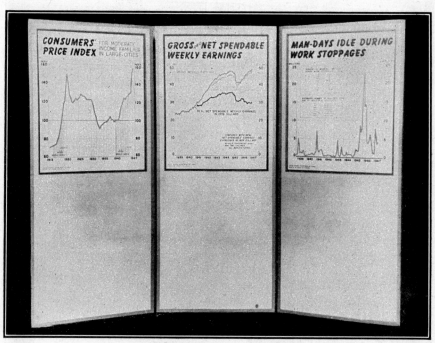

Courtesy of U.S. Department of Labor.

Fig. 9-5. Three-fold screen.

Three-dimensional Exhibit

A striking exhibit was made by cutting out life-size photographic blow-ups of workers and placing them against a background representing a chart. This gave a three-dimensional, lifelike appearance. The small picture in the background could be either a fixed photograph or a mechanical exhibit. The trend plotted on the grid gave a statistical slant to the display.

Courtesy of U.S. Department of Labor.

Fig. 9-6. Three-dimensional exhibit.

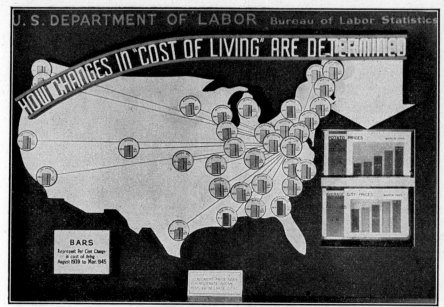

Fig. 9-7. Cutout display and Davis machine.

Fig. 9-8. Mechanical book.

Mechanical Devices

The Davis machine is the most commonly used of the mechanical display devices. It is simple to operate and gives a continuous, moving exhibit. The pictures are fitted into frames which rotate; one dropping in front of the other exposes the next frame. In Fig. 9-7, the Davis machine ran a detailed story on how changes in cost of living are ascertained. The circles on the large relief map located the cities where data were collected. The bars within the circles represented the per cent change in the cost of living from August, 1939, to March, 1945. In making charts for the Davis machine, keep in mind the short length of time that each picture is exposed. Charts should be in their simplest form—bar, column, or simple surface. Titles should be kept short and supplementary lettering at a minimum. If text is necessary, it should be brief and to the point.

Figure 9-8 resembles a large book whose pages automatically turn at regular intervals. This time interval is longer than that at which the Davis machine is usually set, and more material can thus be displayed.

The mechanical man shown in Fig. 9-9 not only moved his arms and head, but he also seemed to speak. A concealed record player and amplifier supplied the voice. As the man moved his arm to point to the different displays, his remarks called attention to the most important aspects of the exhibit, pointing out panels and revolving transparencies.

Courtesy of U.S. Department of Labor.

Fig. 9-9. Mechanical man.

The Economic Analyzer

The Economic Analyzer (patent pending) was invented by Ivan Tarnowsky. It is an example of special equipment primarily designed for businessmen to analyze visually the effect of general business conditions upon a particular firm.

The mechanical aspect of the board is particularly adapted to showing only essentials. Details appear and disappear, showing breakdowns of the story as needed.

One side of the board represents the particular firm and the other side represents all firms in the country. By turning to either side both may be discussed as the analysis progresses.

The graphic flow is laid out with the aid of pegs with attached cords which are held taut by the use of weights or springs. These cords visually outline the flow of cash and the two factors that account for changes in consumer demand. Arrows point to the direction of the flow.

Generally, business men are interested in predicting their sales in the near future. The Economic Analyzer (Fig. 9-10) visualizes very simply the two main factors that need to be forecast.

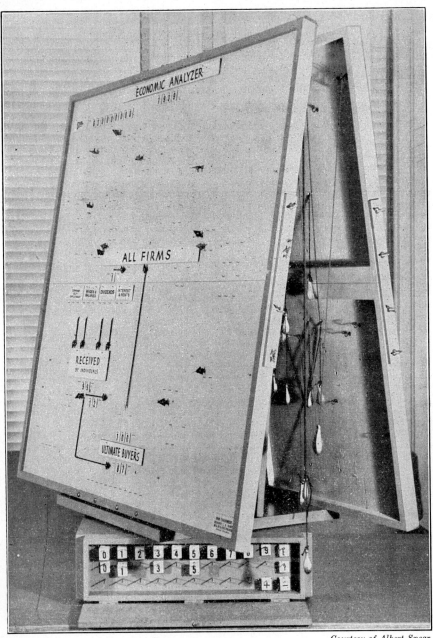

Courtesy of Albert Spear.

Fig. 9-10. Economic Analyzer.

Chart Rooms

When planning a chart or control room, it is advisable to make a layout to scale. First, the visual media should be organized according to type, and then ample space allocated for their particular use.

Figure 9-11 is a photograph of a cardboard model illustrated and painted in color. The floor plan was approximately 15 by 18 inches. The side walls and map section folded over, making a compact working model which was easy to carry. The long conference table was attached to the far wall and collapsed, when the model was folded, in much the same way as a child's pop-up book.

Courtesy of Albert Spear.

Fig. 9-11. Model of chart room (right side).

The right wall was designed for the presentation of statistical data. The far wall served as a map case, the maps sliding behind the wall panels that had been especially designed for them. The maps could be filed away to leave in full view a moving-picture screen that could be raised or lowered as needed. The left wall contained detail maps, special working drawings, and an organization chart. A table along the left wall displayed a relief map and movable models.

On the floor, space was marked where exhibit easels were to stand and where slide and film-strip projectors were to be set up in correct focus.

The moving-picture camera was to be placed in an adjoining room with the wall so designed that the image could be thrown on the projection screen.

Fig. 9-12. Model of chart room (left side).

This made a compact and workable visual-aid room.

A chart room makes an ideal place for a conference, as all pertinent data are at hand for immediate reference. Figures 9-13 and 9-14 show two views of the original chart room of the Bureau of Labor Statistics in Washington. It was familiarly called "Oscar"—short for Operating Statistical Chart Analysis Room.

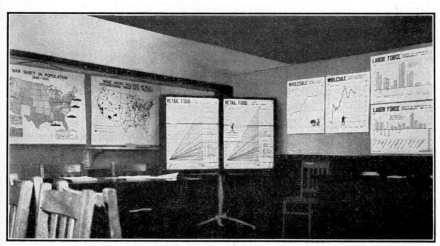

Fig. 9-13. Corner of BLS chart room.

The charts were in color, illustrated, and made on Columbia cloth and Strathmore board. Monk's cloth was stretched on frames, and charts were hung by means of pin hooks fastened on the backs of the bristolboard charts.

Through periodic revisions of the charts, a complete economic and statistical story was kept up to date.

Courtesy of Albert Spear.

Fig. 9-14. Another view of "Oscar."

American University Exhibit

Exhibits range from a simple panel or table display to an elaborate presentation employing many types of visual aids.

In an exhibit in the School of Social Sciences and Public Affairs at the American University in Washington, D.C., both audio and visual aids were shown. The purpose of this exhibit was to stimulate interest in the use of visual techniques to communicate facts and ideas in the field of social science. Included in the exhibit were examples of wall charts, diagrams, relief maps, models, posters, cartoons, slide films, silent motion pictures, audio-motion pictures, and different types of projection equipment.

The attendance showed that not only economists, statisticians, and social scientists, but also other professional and business people are interested in visual aids. The wide interest in this field was also indicated by the great number of teachers and persons working in visual aids who attended this exhibit. This ever-increasing interest forewarns that the inferior, the carelessly conceived chart will no longer pass muster.

Courtesy of Albert Spear.

Fig. 9-15. Wall charts, American University exhibit.

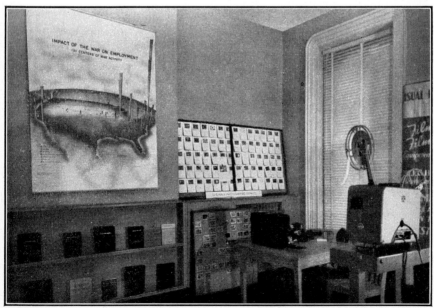

Courtesy of Albert Spear.

Fig. 9-16. Audio-visual aids, American University exhibit.

10 • DUPLICATING COLOR TELEVISION

DUPLICATING

When material is to be duplicated, the process should not be chosen until the number of copies needed has been estimated.

Reproduction in Black and White

1. *From an original in black and white.* The original chart or line drawing must be on opaque paper, with hand or mechanical lettering, and with line work well defined. For a specified number of copies the following processes may be used.

Process	Number of copies feasible	Size of original	Size of reproduced page
PHOTOSTAT	1–15	Up to 29 × 37¾ in.	Up to 18 × 24 in.
OZALID	1–25	Any length and up to 54 in. wide	Same as original
OFFSET: Multilith			
a. Direct-image	26–5,000	Up to 11½ × 14 in.	Same as original
b. Photographic-image	500–25,000	Up to 30 × 40 in.	Up to 17 × 21 in.
LETTERPRESS		Any enlargement	
LITHOGRAPHY	Indefinite	or reduction	
GRAVURE			

If the original charts are lettered with Fototype or any other stack or stick-on lettering and with applied shading or halftones, the offset process of multilith, letterpress, gravure, or lithography should be used (see Fig. 1-9B). The Ben Day process, a mechanical tint of geometric patterns, is applied to the negative by the printer to give shadings on a line cut.

When the mimeograph or ditto method is used, original drawings are made directly on the stencil or processed carbon paper. About 5,000 copies may be made by the mimeograph or stencil process and up to 150 by the hectograph or ditto method.

2. *From original in color.* If charts made in color are to be reproduced, trends should be drawn in line symbols (see Fig. 2-12), as several solid lines cannot be identified in the reproduced copies. Red, orange, green, brown, violet, and their shades will reproduce black or near-black.

Airbrushed bars and columns or map areas may be differentiated by using a solid color for one item and individual shading pattern for each of the other items or categories.

Crosshatched patterns may be made by masking bars or areas or by stripping tape at a desired slant over the space to be airbrushed. Removing the tape leaves the colored crosshatching. Using different widths of tape will vary the crosshatching and avoid making too many different patterns.

Color Reproduction

When the charts are to be reproduced in color, it should be remembered that each color adds greatly to the original cost. Letterpress reproduction is unexcelled in uniformity and stability of color, but is the most expensive process, mostly because of the length of time required to prepare the plates. Gravure is capable of printing color on cheap paper. Offset printing runs low in cost, but the number of impressions in color is limited.

The Craftint Multicolor Process consists of a set of three processed drawing boards or acetate films bearing invisible Ben Day type screens, both dot and line. These screens are properly angled to print one over another without moiré. When used for three-color printing, sixty-three different color combinations are possible. The invisible multicolor tones are instantly "brought up" with the application of multicolor developers, permitting a light and dark tone in addition to a solid and white for each board used. If the film is used, no photography is required in making the color plates.

THE CHART IN COLOR

When an original chart is designed for color, its use and the material it is to be made on will control the method of applying the color.

When color is used, see that it is justified, that it serves a genuine need. For instance, on a map the similarities may be seen more quickly in color than by matching up crosshatched patterns. But the fewer the colors the better.

Color Blindness

In using color, however, the chance of color blindness must be considered. The most common type of color blindness is that of not distinguishing between red and green. Therefore, blue and yellow are, as a rule, safer to use for important hearings and conferences. A deep chrome yellow and dark cobalt blue on a light-gray background can be distinguished at a distance and are pleasing to the eye.

Avoid using very deep or dark colors, as it is difficult to tell them apart even at a short distance.

Methods of Applying Color

If the area to be covered is fairly small, it should be filled in by hand with transparent water colors, poster paints, colored pencils, crayons, or similar media.

For a large area, airbrushing is the most effective semimechanical method of applying the color. The airbrush spray produces an even, solid tone with sharp outline; a blending of one color with another; or a shadowing of one portion in such a way as to stand out from the rest of the chart. It offers, too, the chance to use a variety of colors and their tints and shades.

Airbrush water colors may be sprayed on almost any material with a good "body," such as bristolboard, poster board, Columbia cloth, or water-base window shade. However, care must be taken in removing the mask so that the working surface of the material used may not be damaged. Masking the area to be airbrushed may be done with frisket papers, Scotch tape, or rubber-based products. Only acetate paint will adhere to an acetate surface.

Color on the Negative

A striking and economical display can be made on very short notice by coloring negative photostat copies of charts or maps. This method was followed for a meeting at which the material was to be displayed on panels. Since there was little time for the making of original charts, negative photostat copies were made of selected charts that were on hand.

First the trend lines and light areas on the negative were rubbed over lightly with a plastic eraser. Then Dr. Martin's transparent water colors were applied to the curves and small areas. Care was taken not to have too much color on the brush, as photograph paper will warp. Bright and clear colors were used, because too dark a color could not be distinguished against the black background. For larger areas, such as bars and columns, the desired patterns were cut out of colored Para-Screen or Zip-a-Tone sheets and burnished on the negative.

These clear, brilliant, and harmonizing colors made a dramatic display on the panels.

Colored tape and Zip-a-Tone. Scotch tape, which comes in a variety of colors and widths, may be stripped on for bars and trends.

Sheets of Zip-a-Tone are obtainable in about nine colors. These are most satisfactory when used on bristolboard or material not to be rolled. The desired shape is cut out and simply rubbed or burnished on the chart. The colors are clear and brilliant, but consideration should be

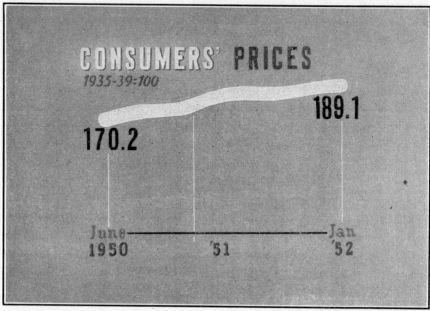

A. MATERIAL USED: Craftint Super White No. 37; Marabu Cool Grays; Light Gray Title Board.

B. MATERIAL USED: Craftint Super White No. 37; Craftint Retouch Grays; No. 96 Mounting Board.

Fig. 10-1. Charts for television.

given to the choice of color combinations. They should be distinctive but not clashing. Two colors of similar intensity and value, as bright red and bright green, may give a blurred result, but darken one and lighten the other and the result will be a striking contrast. Two examples of good combination would be deep red and Nile green, or peach and bottle green.

Color on Acetate

During the World War II a number of acetate overlays were made for a basic chart for Selective Service and the Military Affairs Committee. It was necessary that the colors on these overlays be transparent and at the same time removable. The simplest solution for this particular problem, at that time, proved to be the cutting out of the desired shapes from colored cellophane paper and applying it with rubber cement to the acetate. The durability of this method was surprising. The subsequent amount of handling and rolling of the charts did not damage them. The brilliancy of the colors was most effective, and they could be removed or changed at will.

New gelatinized, transparent water colors that can be applied to acetate surfaces are now on the market. They can be obtained from most art- and drafting-supplies stores. The brilliant colors can be blended with each other or lightened by dilution with water.

TELEVISION

Charts and Titles on TV

Graphic presentation on television presents new problems in style and color. Statistical charts should be simple in construction and bold in design. The fewer details, the better, as the chart appears for only a matter of seconds on the screen. The chart made with white paint on dark-gray paper or board with light-gray Gothic or Roman lettering will stand out prominently on the screen. This same background and lettering should be used for flip-cards and title cards.

All charts, pictures, and cards should be the same size for the same show and kept in the three-to-four ratio demanded by the screen.

Reflection of Light

Glossy prints, glass-covered pictures, and acetate overlay on charts do not televise well and are sometimes completely obscured or flashed out by the light reflection. But if circumstances require their use, they should either be placed in one spot or held steadily before the camera at the angle which will reflect as little light as possible. Rehearsal with camera and lights will determine ahead of time which position is best.

Mat prints and pictures with sharp contrasts are the most satisfactory. It is important that at least a 2- to 4-inch margin be left around mounted pictures when they are to be used for close-ups before the camera.

Animation

Animation adds interest to a statistical presentation or economic report. There are many tricks to gain this extra attention. A strip cartoon in grays and white, moved slowly in front of the camera either by hand or mechanically on a revolving drum, can add humor to a report.

Movable models of persons or objects, as automobiles, houses, etc., against a blow-up background relating to the story, may describe the situation of unemployment, strikes, and housing conditions. Tanks, soldiers, planes, and ships being moved across a map will dramatize a historical event.

The flannel board with cut-outs is a speedy and interest-holding method of presenting statistical information. A five-ply board is covered with a dark-gray blanket or flannel on which charts or pictorial objects, backed with sandpaper, are placed. The sandpaper-backed cutouts adhere to the flannel with a little pressure and downward movement. With this device the picture can be built up one piece at a time as the story progresses.

Use of Color on TV

If color must be used before the television camera, avoid red and its varying shades. Green, blue, brown, and blue-violet televise best. Solid black will "spill over" and does not give a clean line definition. When possible, keep presentations in shades of gray and white. Remember that simplicity is the first rule in any presentation.

INDEX

La Bi

WHICH CHART TO USE ?
THE DATA

Motor Buses in Operation in United States

Year	Intercity Buses	Local Buses (1)	Charter and Sightseeing Buses	School Buses (2)	Total Buses
1941	18,420	37,855	2,383	87,400	146,058
1942	22,710	44,101	2,400	79,000	148,211
1943	28,504	45,610	2,000	77,850	153,964
1944	28,000	48,525	3,300	75,500	153,964
1945	29,000	45,955	3,300	75,500	155,325
1946	30,260	47,760	1,033	83,228	159,216
1947	31,900	54,100	1,475	82,500	161,995
1948	31,775	57,175	3,000	85,900	174,900
1949	30,200	57,800	3,200	90,400	182,550
			3,500	97,600	189,100

① Omits trolley buses.   ② Exclusive of common carrier buses doing schoolwork.

SOURCE: "Bus Transportation" as of December 31st.

THE CURVE CHART

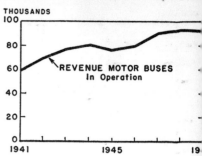

THOUSANDS

REVENUE MOTOR BUSES
In Operation

THE GROUPED COLUMN

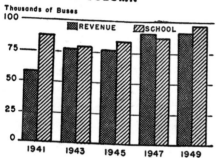

Thousands of Buses

REVENUE   SCHOOL

THE BAR CHART

1949

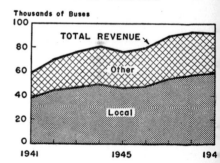

Thousands of Buses

SCHOOL — 98
LOCAL — 58
INTERCITY — 30
CHARTER & SIGHTSEEING — 4

THE CUMULATIVE CURVE

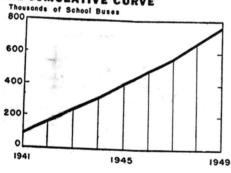

Thousands of School Buses

THE SUBDIVIDED SURFACE

Thousands of Buses

TOTAL REVENUE

Other

Local

THE SLIDING BAR

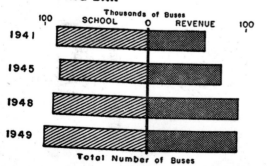

Thousands of Buses

SCHOOL   O   REVENUE

1941
1945
1948
1949

Total Number of Buses

THE PICTOGRAM

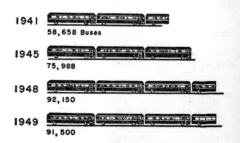

1941   58,658 Buses
1945   75,988
1948   92,150
1949   91,500